CLAIRE ORTALDA

P9-CFM-249

FOG CITY FUNDAMENTALS

A Proofreading Skills Book

Third Edition

Editors

Kevin Conway
Michele Driscoll
Jan Gregory
Dan Petersen
Leslie Roberts
William S. Robinson
Randall Roorda
Stephen Stedman

Gary Anderberg, *Artist*

English Department
San Francisco State University

San Francisco, California

BURGESS INTERNATIONAL GROUP INC
Bellwether Press Division

Copyright © 1988, 1987, 1986 by Burgess International Group, Inc.,
Bellwether Press Division
ISBN 0-8087-6981-1

All rights reserved. No part of this book may be reproduced in any form whatsoever,
by photograph or xerography or by any other means, by broadcast or transmission, by
translation into any kind of language, nor by recording electronically or otherwise,
without permission in writing from the publisher, except by a reviewer, who may
quote brief passages in critical articles and reviews.

Printed in the United States of America.
Q

Address orders to:

Burgess International Group, Inc.
7110 Ohms Lane
Edina, MN 55435
Telephone 612/831-1344
Telex 29-0458

Bellwether Press
A Division of Burgess International Group, Inc.

PREFACE

Fog City Fundamentals was designed so it can be used on a "needs" basis—for individualized work suited to the needs of individual students. It begins with verbs and other sentence-level issues, since many students seem to want and need to begin with work at the sentence level. But some students may best be served by working first on apostrophes, homonyms or other sections on usage which come nearer the end of the book, while others may have mastered verbs and need to focus on, for example, sentence fragments. Some students will need to do many of the exercises in the book, others fewer. The book may be used in the classroom but it is not the basis for a whole course; it is not a substitute for carefully selected and sequenced work in composition but an adjunct to that work, a text that will not solve everyone's problems but that should make everyone's life a little easier.

The purpose of the text is not to teach writing as such but to help students develop the skills that will make them better proofreaders of their own work, to refine their knowledge of the basic conventions of written English, and to sharpen their ability to see what they have actually written. It aims to help students understand when their work needs proofreading and how to proofread effectively.

We realize that we have in all likelihood not covered every issue dear to every instructor's heart, and we have no doubt failed to discover the peculiarities in each exercise. But we have intentionally omitted more sophisticated issues of sentence construction: this is a basic-skills proofreading text only.

To paraphrase Lincoln, "you can please some of the people some of the time . . ." We hope the book is user-friendly, and that you are among the "some" who will be pleased. We also invite comment, preferably constructive even if critical, from students and teachers alike.

Our special thanks to Nancy McDermid, San Francisco State University's Dean of Humanities, for her help in making available to us the funds needed for producing the first edition of this book. Thanks also to Kitty Quinn-Friel, Susan Talton, and Ernie Vasquez for their patience and perseverance in typing the manuscript as it evolved. Most of all we thank all our friends and colleagues whose suggestions and contributions made this book possible, in particular Juan Aninao, Nadine DeVost, Elise Earthman, Kathleen Josephson, Loretta Kane, Patricia Low, Catharine Lucas, Barbara McClure, Claudia Mon Pere, Patricia Porter, Susan Skov.

Making Proofreading Easier

1. Keep this book and a dictionary handy when you're proofreading—and use them.

2. Make a list of the problems you have, and refer to it.

3. Isolate problems and solve them one at a time.

4. Type and double-space your final copy so it's easier for you to read.

5. Mask off the parts of the page that interfere with what you want to focus on.

PROOFREADING TIPS

All teachers and prospective employers want you to write well, and will think better of you if you can. They want you to organize your ideas clearly, keep your focus on your main ideas, and use specifics to develop those ideas.

They also want your written work to follow the "rules of the road." You can achieve this goal by allowing more time for *proofreading* your work. Most of us need to proofread several times, with different goals each time. This part of the book shows you some techniques for doing the job more effectively.

For starters, keep this book handy when you're revising or proofreading your written work. The table of contents will help you find the units relevant to you. Also make and keep handy a list of problems your teacher marks on your essays or paragraphs. Techniques that may help you *spot* them are suggested below; the rest of the book will show you how to correct them.

The first step in proofreading is to decide what you're looking for—to focus on one thing at a time. If you try to proofread the paper as a whole, you'll just get confused, but if you *isolate problems* and deal with them one at a time, you'll find it easier.

For instance, let's say you have had problems with verbs. Isolate every verb: find and *underline* all of them. If aren't sure whether some word is a verb, check "Recognizing Verbs." Once you're sure, find the subject of the verb; if you need help isolating the subject, look up "Recognizing Subjects."

Read the sentences one at a time and ask yourself whether you have used the appropriate verb ending:

1) Is the *tense* correctly indicated? (The wrong form will mislead the reader about the time when an action or event occurred.)

2) Does each present-tense verb *agree* with its subject?

It's sometimes hard to decide what form a verb should have. To figure out which is most appropriate, read the entire paragraph and then ask yourself these questions about each verb: "Is this about an event that took place in the past and is now completed? An event that is occurring right now? Something that will happen in the future?" In other words, what is the time-frame each verb should show? (For use of certain past forms, look up "Special Tenses," the unit that explains two special kinds of verb forms.)

Similar proofreading tips appear at the end of many units of the book. Use these hints to find out the "legal" ways of finding and correcting the errors in your work.

It may be easier for you to proofread your work if you *mask off* the parts of the page that keep you from focusing on the sentence or paragraph you're proofreading; just take a blank sheet of paper and cover the rest of the page. It will definitely be easier for you to proofread if you *double-space* all the work you do, and if you *type* your work. Especially when you're checking spelling, apostrophes, capitalization, omitted words, and "silly mistakes" or "careless errors," it will be much easier if you have double-spaced and typed so that you can see each word clearly.

Doing all this will take a while. The more you do it, though, the quicker you'll become at doing each step of the process, and the more skillful you'll become at seeing and then correcting errors. The payoff will be work you can feel good about—something we all want, and learn to produce only after repeated experience.

GRANT AVENUE GATE - CHINATOWN

TABLE OF CONTENTS

I. VERBS AND SUBJECTS

RECOGNIZING VERBS

The following paragraph is written in the present tense. Rewrite it by changing the verbs into the past tense.

      Autumn is my favorite time of year. The leaves turn orange, yellow and red, and then fall to the ground. The air is crisp and smells of smoke. In the store, huge apples and pumpkins crowd the shelves, and on campus, students are unusually cheerful. They know they have a few sunny, relaxing weekends left before cold weather and term papers.

Past tense: _____

_____

_____

_____

_____

_____

Some people believe that verbs are words that express action, but this is often not true.

VERBS ARE WORDS THAT CHANGE THEIR FORMS TO INDICATE THE TENSE OR TIME OF A SENTENCE.

Look at this sentence: Swimming is my favorite sport.

What is the action word? What word changes if you put the sentence in past time? So what is the verb?

Exercise 1

Locate verbs in the sentences below by rewriting each sentence twice, first in the past and then in the future (using "will"). Underline the verbs in your rewritten sentences.

    Example: Molly loves quizzes.

                         Molly *loved* quizzes. (past)

                         Molly *will love* quizzes. (future)

---

1. Mike's history teacher puts a time-table for the hour of the midterm up on the board.

2. Mike stares at his exam questions a few minutes.

3. After doing this, he begins to write a few notes on his paper.

4. The question about WW II is by far the most complicated.

5. Mike knows his history well.

6. First he sets up a chronological outline of key events.

7. Three of the four main points flash through his mind.

8. After 5 minutes, Mike opens his book and starts to write.

9. He finishes 40 minutes later, checks his essay, and reads it over for errors.

RECOGNIZING SUBJECTS

Once you can locate the verb in a sentence, it is easy to find the subject of the verb.

THE SUBJECT IS THE WORD THAT ANSWERS THE QUESTION *WHO* OR *WHAT* IN RELATION TO THE VERB.

The storm rages in California. (What rages?)
George is beating on the door. (Who is beating?)
The car over there is mine. (What is mine?)
Mary and Suzette are no longer roommates. (Who are not roommates?)
Regular lubrication and maintenance are necessary to keep a car in good shape. (What is necessary?)

As a review, underline each of the verbs in the paragraph once.

Autumn is my favorite time of year. The leaves turn orange, yellow and red, and then fall to the ground. The air is crisp and smells of smoke. In the store, huge pumpkins crowd the shelves, and on campus, students are unusually cheerful. They know they have a few sunny, relaxing weekends left before cold weather and term papers.

Now go back and underline the subjects of the verbs twice.

The only tricky part about identifying subjects comes when there is more than one noun in front of the verb.

The *sweater* in the *drawer* is made of wool.

Usually the "who or what" question will solve the problem. Who or what is made of wool—the sweateer or the drawer? In this case it's obvious. But sometimes the "who or what" question can be misleading:

The *hole* in the sweater will have to be fixed.

Who or what will have to be fixed—*hole* or *sweater*? In this situation, the noun nearest the front of the sentence is the subject—in this case, *hole. Sweater* is not the subject even though it also makes sense to say that the sweater will have to be fixed.

"In the drawer" and "in the sweater" are special groups of words called prepositional phrases. A few prepositions are *in, of, at, by,* and *from.* The noun *after* a preposition cannot be the subject of a sentence or clause.

4

TEMPLE LION
AT THE
DE YOUNG MUSEUM

Exercise 2

Locate the subjects in the following sentences; first locate the *verb* and underline it once, and then find the *subject* and underline it twice.

1. The peaches on the tree are ripe now.

2. The growers in my county will be harvesting soon.

3. My sister and her friend supervise the workers.

4. At the side of the plant, two old warehouses store the packed fruit for shipping.

5. Several people in my class work in the warehouse at night.

6. Some of the workers in the warehouse look for spoiled fruit.

7. My best friend's parents sold their orchards last year to a speculator.

8. Flowers and weeds are growing in their fields now.

9. Like most retired couples, they want to go south and enjoy the sun.

10. Meanwhile the work of watering, pruning and harvesting the different crops keeps going on.

Exercise 3

Underline the *verb* or *verb phrase* in each of the following sentences once and the *subject* of each twice.

---

1. The automobile crashed directly into the wall.

2. Jogging and swimming are fantastic exercise for both men and women.

3. The basketball player from Union High School plays like a pro and looks good too.

4. The reference confuses many students.

5. Water is becoming scarce in many parts of the country.

6. The ants in the big tank burrowed many tunnels.

7. He was mugging the old man.

8. At the concert, Miles Davis will play the trumpet.

9. The earthquake and the fire destroyed San Francisco overnight.

10. Everyone will vote in the election.

RECOGNIZING VERBS AND SUBJECTS

Post-Test

In the passage below, underline the verb of each sentence once and its subject twice.

Cindy and I wanted to get away from the city for a while, so last week we took a trip to Yosemite. Leaving the city, we talked excitedly about visiting the wilderness and breathing some fresh air for a change. We were hoping for peace and solitude, but we were disappointed. The road into the park twisted through rock piles and turned along a river; ahead of us we saw long lines of cars. The crowds in the park itself kept us away from the waterfalls. Hungry and tired, we tried to get into the cafeteria but left because of the mile-long lines. Wanting to take a scenic tour, we discovered yet more lines; every seat on the tour bus was already reserved. We finally gave up and headed for home. Getting away from civilization was not as easy as we had hoped.

II. COMPLETE SENTENCES

DIFFERENT GROUPS OF WORDS

Phrases and Clauses

We have names for different kinds of word-groups composed of different "ingredients." As an example, read the following two groups of words:

1. Birds from the big tree.

2. Birds fly from the big tree.

What is the difference between these two groups of words? In the second we can identify a subject/verb unit while in the first we cannot.

* Remember to find the verb first by changing a word in the sentence into another time-frame: past or future.

   Birds *flew* from the big tree.
   Birds *will fly* from the big tree.

* Then find the subject by asking, "Who or what flew?" *Birds.* If we try to change 1 (above) into past or future time, we can't—it contains no word that can be altered to show a change in time. In other words, 1 has no verb.

We call a group of words with a subject/verb unit a *clause;* a group of words without a subject/verb unit is a *phrase*.

* The *-ing* form of a word cannot be a verb *all by itself*.

   The sweat dripping from his forehead

is not a clause, but a phrase. What must you add in front of *dripping* so that you can put this word-group in past tense? _____ . The -ing form of a verb must have a helping verb to function as a complete verb.

   The sweat *was dripping* from his forehead.

** *A special kind of phrase:* It's obvious that "happy people" is a phrase. But so is "people who are happy." There is a special kind of phrase that follows this pattern:

   noun + *who* . . . . . .   people who are happy
   noun + *which* . . . . . .   habits which annoy me
   noun + *that* . . . . . .   beliefs that most people share
                      beliefs (that are) shared by most people

Even though these structures contain a verb, they are still considered phrases because the noun before the *who, which,* or *that* structure does not have its own verb.

8

We do use these structures as *parts* of sentences:

> *The girl who sits next to me in math class* knows my sister.

> I know *the girl who sits next to me in math class.*

THE PALACE OF THE LEGION OF HONOUR — LINCOLN PARK

Exercise 1

Which of the following groups of words are phrases? Which are clauses? Label each one.

___

1. a long, unpleasant, tiring journey

2. teachers have no sense of humor at all

3. teachers with no sense of humor at all

4. thinking about how to pass the course

5. rear tires spinning and engine roaring

6. students were lying all over the grass

7. the creep in my psychology class

8. a small town northeast of San Jose

9. flying down to South America in a huge Boeing 747 with nothing under my coat but some flimsy underwear and a scar from my appendectomy

10. he forgot his wallet

11. my girlfriend loves me

12. a girl who loves me

13. cruising down Market Street in his Porsche

14. a trait that I share with many others

15. I share my money with my friends

16. her hair blowing in the wind

17. a world in which nobody listens to anybody else

18. a friend who has known me from childhood hurt me very badly

19. rooms full of old paper, rusty kitchen equipment, broken furniture, and quite a few dead mice

Two Kinds of Clauses

You now know what a clause is, but there are two kinds of clauses you need to know about: dependent and independent. What's the difference? Read the examples below and then explain in your own words how they are different.

1.   Mary likes the clown.   (independent clause)

2.   Because Mary likes the clown.   (dependent clause)

Words like *because* are called subordinators. When we use subordinating words at the beginning of a clause, the clause becomes dependent and can no longer stand alone. Dependent clauses should always be attached to independent clauses.

Some Common Subordinators

as	wherever	as if
as long as	while	as though
as soon as	though	because
after	although	since
before	even though	so that
by the time	even if	that
until	if	who/whom
when	unless	whose
whenever	whether	which

Exercise 2

Identify the following as independent or dependent clauses.

1. whenever I feel bored

2. she proposed to me

3. although I am her cousin

4. Charles says he loves me

5. because I was tired

6. before the semester began

7. while I was sitting on that park bench

8. I intend to finish college

9. after Arlene left for Chicago

10. wherever you may go

11. since Mary and Jack got married

12. I hate to write

13. unless you stop doing that right now

14. even though Sherry knows

SENTENCE FRAGMENTS

Sentence fragments are *phrases* or *dependent clauses* punctuated as if they were complete sentences.

Exercise 3

In each exercise below, identify each group of words as a *sentence* or *fragment*.

1. since I had nothing else for lunch today except a hamburger
2. if I could be alone to work on my homework
3. rain in May is something I do not expect
4. a wonderful person with all kinds of unusual talents and accomplishments
5. especially people who are selfish
6. success comes to people who work hard
7. although I do not enjoy hard work
8. when exams are just around the corner
9. because the afternoon was cold enough for a sweater
10. I wish you would begin at the beginning of a story

Exercise 4

1. before the darkest part of the evening
2. a laboratory for the study of animal life in the South Pacific
3. we all worked on making the lunch for the whole group
4. many times in the past I have gone to his parties
5. enjoyable, crowded parties with good music, many people, and wonderful food and wine
6. such as snakes, rats, and insects

7. an idea which I find difficult to understand

8. after I came home ready to sleep for a while

9. his eyes staring vacantly ahead

10. good friends all the way through college, both in San Francisco and Los Angeles

Exercise 5

In each of the following pairs, underline the fragment.

---

1. College is much more difficult than high school. Even though one spends fewer hours in class each day.

2. I dislike teachers who grade unfairly. Especially those who give higher grades to their favorite students.

3. Helena studies at least five hours every day. Always trying to keep up her G.P.A.

4. Because most people who watch MTV on a regular basis are very young. Performers such as Frank Sinatra and Peggy Lee do not appear on this music channel.

5. I study on weekends. Because on weekdays I work at Woolworth after my classes are over.

6. I am taking a number of difficult courses this semester. For example, Spanish, economics and microbiology.

7. I only sleep four hours a night. Which is not enough sleep for me to feel alert the next day.

8. I am majoring in business. A very difficult and time-consuming major.

Explain what you notice about the position of most of the fragments in relationship to the sentences.

Most fragments *follow* the sentences to which they should be attached. Some people automatically put a period at the end of each sentence. Without waiting until they decide whether they want to add more to the sentence. In doing this, they often create a fragment—as I just did. Can you spot it? Identify it by underlining it.

Because most fragments follow the sentences to which they should be attached, they are easy to correct. Simply join them to the sentences they follow.

Exercise 6

Now *correct* the sentences in Exercise 5.

PROOFREADING FOR FRAGMENTS

In going over an essay or a paragraph, look at every group of words that begins with a capital letter and ends with a period. Is each one a complete sentence? (How can you tell? Reread "Sentence Fragments," on p. 13.) If it is not complete, look at the group of words that comes before it AND the one that follows. The incomplete group should probably be attached to one of them. Decide which one it goes with, and make the necessary changes, or add the "missing ingredients" to complete the incomplete sentence. HINT: It may help you to read out loud when you're trying to decide whether a group of words is complete or incomplete. We can often *hear* it when something sounds incomplete.

Exercise 7

Underline any sentence fragments (parts of sentences punctuated as if they were complete sentences) that you find in the following passages.

I share a room with my sister. The messiest person in the world. My side of the room is always neat and clean. While her side always looks terrible. As if it just went through a major earthquake. She never hangs up her clothes. When she takes them off. The floor is her closet. For over a year now the top of her dresser hasn't been seen by human eyes. It is covered with dirty gym socks, old Coke cans, crumpled pieces of paper, and old tubes of dried-out lipstick. Without any tops on them. Her bed is piled high with wrinkled clothing. Covered from head to foot with her junk. Once I even cleaned part of the room for her, but two days later it looked like the city dump again. Which was not very encouraging. Thinking about this for a long time. I have decided she will have to marry a rich man. Someone who can afford a housekeeper.

FRAGMENTS

Post-Test

Find and underline any fragments in the following passage. (Some people feel that it is easier to spot fragments—especially in their own writing—if they read the passage backwards: first, the last sentence, then, the next-to-last, and so on.)

Then, on a separate sheet of paper, rewrite the passage to eliminate the fragments by joining them to the proper sentences.

Everyone is prejudiced in some way. Even those who think they aren't. Some prejudices are serious. While others are silly. I am prejudiced against crew-cuts. This prejudice developed when I was a teenager. Beginning in junior high school. When I was in the seventh grade, crew-cuts came into fashion. Soon every boy in my class had one. Except me. I had always been very popular with my classmates. Especially with those in the "in-group." Because I was friendly and bright. Suddenly, however, I was no longer popular because I no longer had the right "look." Even though my mother claimed she loved me. She would not let me get my hair cut short in the popular style. Because she thought that crew-cuts were terrible looking. I pleaded with her but she still refused. I was desperate. Because I wanted to look like the other guys in the class. The "big shots" who decided what was "in" and what was "out." I guess I should have learned a lesson from this experience. That people who judge you by your appearance aren't worth having as friends. Something that you can't tell a seventh-grader. All I knew was that not having a crew cut made me less popular than I had been. I've hated crew-cuts ever since.

III. RUN-TOGETHER SENTENCES

People often write run-together sentences when they see that two thoughts belong together *logically* but *don't* realize that the two thoughts are separate sentences *grammatically*. Run-together sentences (RTS for short) occur when two sentences are joined with no punctuation between them or with only a comma connecting them.

> It rained every day we never left the hotel.
> It rained every day, we never left the hotel.

What are the two sentences in each of the examples here? RTS's are often confusing for the reader, who normally does not expect to see sentences joined this way and must stop to sort out what's going on.

Preliminary Exercise

Often the second sentence in the run-together begins with one of the following words, because these words often refer to something in the first sentence:

I	we	there	now
you	they	this	then
he		that	
she			
it			

Write a second sentence to go with each sentence below. Start the second sentence with the word given to the left of each sentence.

_____

(They)   1.   I could not find my car keys. _____

_____

(Then)   2.   The first thing Bill ate for dessert was a peach. _____

_____

(She)   3.   My daughter began screaming. _____

_____

(It)   4.   The toaster oven was acting strangely. _____

_____

(There)   5.   Cars had to stop suddenly at the intersection. _____

_____

18

Generally, we consider it wise to join sentences which are this closely related logically but we must use more than just a comma or no punctuation at all. We don't want choppy sentences, but we don't want run-togethers, either.

WAYS OF CORRECTING RUN-TOGETHER SENTENCES

* *Use a coordinator.* Usually run-together sentences occur because the two sentences within them are so closely related to each other that they *should* be joined in a single sentence. One way of showing how the sentences are related is to join them with a coordinator (one of the "FANBOYS"):

For	*But*
And	*Or*
Nor	*Yet*
	So

I'd like to buy a new car, *but* I can't afford one.

* *Use a subordinator.* You can also show the relationship between two sentences by using a subordinator to change one of them into a *dependent clause:*

Although I'd like to buy a new car, I can't afford one.
I'd like to buy a new car *although* I can't afford one.

* *Use a semi-colon.* As we have seen, a comma is not sufficient to join two sentences. A semi-colon *is* enough, though. In fact, one way of looking at a semi-colon is to think of it as a heavy-duty comma, strong enough to join sentences:

It was nearly sundown; my shadow stretched far ahead on the sidewalk.

Semi-colons are useful for joining sentences that seem to belong together, but are not related in ways easily expressed by coordinators or subordinators. Often such sentences will have different subjects.

Beware: Introductory words or phrases such as *however, then, therefore, moreover, for example,* do *NOT* join sentences. If you begin a sentence with one of these words or phrases, make sure the sentence preceding it ends with a period or a semi-colon.

Exercise 1

One way to correct a run-together sentence is to use a subordinator to make one of the sentences in the run-together a dependent clause. These are some common subordinators:

as	wherever	as if
as long as	while	as though
as soon as	though	because
after	although	since
before	even though	so that
by the time	even if	until
if	when	unless
whenever	whether	

In the following sentences, correct the run-together by adding an appropriate subordinator.

EXAMPLE: <u>Although</u> it was a perfect day for the beach, I had to study all day for my upcoming exams.

My exams went well <u>although</u> I didn't understand the last question on the physics exam.

Note that when you use a subordinator at the beginning of a sentence, you must use a comma to separate the two clauses. You do not use a comma if the dependent clause comes at the end of the sentence.

1. _____ Marge was an "A" student, she didn't have to study for her English midterm.

2. _____ Harry was a good musician, he never could keep a steady job in a band.

3. Gloria knew all the ropes _____ she met Fred.

4. _____ the sunshine in March was pleasant, it was a disaster for local farmers.

5. I was happy _____ my grades arrived in the mail.

6. Sue would buy a new car _____ she had the money.

Exercise 2

Another way to correct a run-together is to use a comma and a coordinator to connect the two complete thoughts. In the exercises below, use one of the seven coordinating conjunctions ("FANBOYS": *for, and, nor, but, or, yet, so*) to join the two sentences.

EXAMPLE: I hate to see animals in cages, <u>so</u> I don't like to go to the zoo.

1. Nick and Fran enjoyed the movie, they wished the seats had been more comfortable.

2. My TV wasn't working, I walked over to a friend's house to watch the game.

3. Fred remembered to get the hamburger he forgot to buy the hamburger rolls.

4. The telephone was ringing, someone was at the front door as well.

5. Brett moved from Boston to Los Angeles, he wanted to get as far away as possible from his ex-wife.

Exercise 3

You can also correct a run-together sentence by inserting a semicolon (;) between the two sentences. In the sentences below, insert a semicolon where the sentences run together.

---

1. The tide had risen three feet by nightfall, waves began to lap across the top of the pier.

2. Something was obviously wrong with the meatloaf, it was glowing in the dark.

3. Mike never heard the third-base coach screaming for him to stop, he was out at home plate by ten feet.

4. Our manager proposed a ten percent reduction in salaries, the staff didn't like the idea.

5. I was happy with my new apartment, it was in a good location and the rent was very low.

Exercise 4

Often, along with a semicolon, a transition (an introductory word or phrase such as *however, then, for example*) may be used to show the relationship between ideas. It is important to remember that it is the *semicolon* which joins the sentences, *not* the transition. A transition can not join sentences in the way that coordinators and subordinators can.

Here is a list of some common transitions:

however	nevertheless	on the other hand
instead	meanwhile	otherwise
indeed	in addition	also
moreover	furthermore	as a result
thus	consequently	therefore
then	for example	

Typically, when a transition is used in two sentences joined with a semicolon, it begins the second clause; in other words, it follows the semicolon. A transition is almost always followed by a comma.

I figured the ball game would cost me about eight dollars; *however*, I didn't consider the price of food and drinks.

But a transition can be used in many different places in a sentence, usually set off by commas. Remember, the transition by itself doesn't *join* sentences.

I figured the ball game would cost me about eight dollars;
I didn't, *however*, consider the price of food and drinks.

Correct the run-togethers below with a semicolon and an appropriate transition from the list above.

1. The tree must be sprayed with insecticide, the spider mites will kill it.

2. I helped the magician set up his props, I agreed to let him saw me in half.

3. Fred never finished paneling his living room, he hired a carpenter to complete the job.

4. My house was robbed last week, I bought a watchdog.

5. Juanita is taking five courses this semester, she is working forty hours a week.

Exercise 5

Correct the following run-together sentences. The best choice would be a logical joining word; the next choice might be a semicolon; the last and worst is the use of a period.

---

1. The Navajos are a nomadic people, the Hopis are farmers.

2. Despite my father's plans for me, I didn't want to study medicine, I wanted to become a teacher.

3. Elaine was very ill, she missed three days of class.

4. The Student Union doesn't have enough tables, many students are forced to eat outside.

5. Bishop Tutu spoke about the problems in South Africa, he stressed the need for speedy solutions to those problems.

6. The book has been on the best-seller list for months, it's one of the most boring novels I've ever read.

7. In an earthquake, buildings sway back and forth, many rattle and groan.

8. Our blood serves as a provider for the body's needs, it carries not only oxygen but also such nutrients as glucose and amino acids to all the tissues of the body.

9. Persons of North European backgrounds generally feel the need for relatively large spatial bubbles around them, those of Mediterranean or Asian backgrounds usually need much smaller ones.

10. The room was filthy, empty beer cans and half-eaten food were scattered all over the floor.

Exercise 6

Correct the following run-together sentences.

---

1. Billie Holliday was one of the greatest jazz singers of all time, she captivated audiences wherever she went.

2. Mark is not very interested in sports, he does, however, like to water-ski.

3. My living room is very small, I should not buy any more furniture.

4. Some students graduate from high school without having learned much of anything, nobody knows exactly whose fault this is.

5. Dedicated ecologists do not kill wildlife, they shoot with cameras instead of guns.

6. Some people are very considerate, others think of nobody but themselves.

7. I can't wait for my mid-terms to be over, then I can finally get some sleep.

8. Jean is my best friend, she is always there for me when I need her.

9. She is not only an excellent student, she is also an outstanding athlete.

10. Although I try very hard to budget my time carefully, I never seem to get things done on time, for example, my essays for English are often late.

Exercise 7

Now that you have practiced several methods of correcting run-together sentences, go back to the Preliminary Exercise at the beginning of this chapter and join each pair of sentences, using one of the methods you've learned. Try to use several different methods. Rewrite the sentences here.

1.

2.

3.

4.

5.

PROOFREADING FOR RUN-TOGETHER SENTENCES

Read your whole essay or paragraph out loud. Pace your reading so that you are not racing or, on the other hand, speaking more slowly than you usually do. Listen carefully as you read, though, so that you can hear each sentence. If you come to the end of a sentence and see a comma, read the words that come after the comma very carefully—out loud. Is the group of words following the comma also a complete sentence? If so, you need to change something. We use commas for many purposes, but one is "illegal"—a comma between two complete sentences when you have not also used a "legal" joining word. (Look up the "legal" joining methods on p. 19.)

THE PALACE OF FINE ARTS - the Marina

28

Exercise 8

The following passage contains run-together sentences. Correct any that you find.

---

① Sleep is a subject we should all know a lot about, [*since*] we spend one third of our lives sleeping. ② [*OK*] Even though everyone sleeps, scientists have only recently begun to understand what goes on when we sleep. ③ They used to believe that the body repairs itself [*only*] while asleep; [*although*] there is some truth to this, ~~but~~ the body also does this while awake. ④ The brain does not simply shut itself off at night; instead, it goes through a complicated series of chemical changes. ⑤ Scientists have begun to chart these changes [*by*] working with complex instruments that measure brain-wave patterns. ⑥ They have found that we do not move smoothly from being awake to being asleep, [*instead*] we pass through a cycle of four sleep stages. ⑦ At each stage blood pressure and pulse rate drop, [*and*] the body temperature also goes down. ⑧ In the second stage, the number and length of brain waves go[*es*] up, while the sleeper's eyes begin to move rapidly back and forth behind their lids. ⑨ Scientists call this ~~activity rapid eye movements, or REM's, the~~ [*REM, or rapid eye mov.*] activity that accompanies most of our dreaming. ⑩ If a person is deprived of REM sleep; [*as a result*] that person will soon become bad-tempered and irritable. A full night's sleep is not a single, unbroken state, but consists of four or five of these multi-stage sleep cycles.

RUN-TOGETHER SENTENCES

Post-Test

The following passage contains run-together sentences. Correct any that you find.

In 1867, a chef at a hotel in Saratoga Springs accidentally dropped some thinly sliced potatoes into hot cooking oil, instantly the world found a new delicacy: the potato chip. At the time, Saratoga Springs was America's most fashionable resort, fads that started there usually found immediate success. Almost overnight, the potato chip became Saratoga's hottest item. The wide, tree-lined avenues were filled with people eating potato chips, the huge veranda of the United States Hotel was no different; it was filled with chip-eaters too. Some of the richest, most powerful people in the world consumed them regularly, for instance, the Vanderbilts could often be seen daintily plucking chips from paper cups on their stroll back to their mansion. The elegant "Saratoga chips" remained the delicacy of the wealthy until 1925, when the first chip factory was constructed in Albany, New York. The potato chip was no longer the snack of only the rich and famous instead it became a common household item. Of course potato chips have changed a great deal in the last hundred years, now they come in various textures and flavors, some even come stacked in paper tubes! Still, the next time you grab a handful of greasy, flavor-dusted chips, you might pause to remember the noble origins of that humble food. It might be the closest you'll ever get to living like the Vanderbilts, you'd better enjoy it!

IV. PRESENT TENSE SUBJECTS AND VERBS

SUBJECT-VERB AGREEMENT A

Look at the following verb forms:

Past	Future
I walked.	I will walk.
You walked.	You will walk.
We walked.	We will walk.
They walked.	They will walk.
He walked.	He will walk.
She walked.	She will walk.
It walked.	It will walk.

In the past and future, most verbs don't change their forms, regardless of their subjects. In the present, however, there is one exception:

Present

I walk.
You walk.
We walk.
They walk.

He walks.   The 3rd person singular verb
She walks.   always has an "s" ending.
It walks.

Although in conversation the "s" in the present tense is sometimes dropped, in written English the "s" must be included.

It is easy to see that when your subject is *he, she,* or *it,* the correct present-tense verb will have an -*s* ending. But what about when the subject of the sentence is *police officer, Shirley,* or *table?*

These nouns—any noun, in fact—can be replaced by a *pronoun,* a word like *he, she,* or *it,* that stands for a noun. If you replace the noun subject of your sentence with a pronoun, you will be able to determine the correct verb form.

Here are the subject pronouns, which you saw earlier:

I	we
he	you
she	they
it	

Any noun can be replaced by one of these pronouns.

So check subject/verb units in this way:

Charles ride the bus every day.

1. Underline the subject and verb:

   Charles ride the bus every day.

2. Replace the subject noun with the appropriate pronoun:

   [Charles = he] *He ride* the bus every day.

is   Since you know that *he-she-it* subjects must have an *-s* ending in the present tense, *he ride* obviously incorrect, so *Charles ride* is also incorrect. The correct sentence would read:

Charles *rides* the bus every day.

* NOTE: We use "s" in many different ways, to show different things. Remember these basic rules:

   1. When we *add* "s" to a singular noun, we are making it plural. For instance, *book* is singular, *books* plural; *shoes* plural; *movie* is singular, *movies* plural.

      But some singular nouns end in "s". Examples are *witness, glass, Charles.*

   2. When we add "s" to a verb, we are showing two things: the verb is 1) singular, and 2) third-person present tense. For example, he look*s*, she smile*s*, the engine work*s*, it seem*s*, grass grow*s*.

SO . . . A verb that has an "s" ending *cannot* be used with a plural noun as its subject.

32

Exercise 1

Column A is a list of subject nouns. First substitute the appropriate pronoun for the subject noun and write it in column B. Then, using the verb in parentheses, make the correct subject/verb combination.

	A	B	(verb)	S/V
Ex.	John	he	(walk)	John walks
1.	children	_____	(sing)	_____
2.	aunt	_____	(look)	_____
3.	tree	_____	(grow)	_____
4.	king	_____	(rule)	_____
5.	Chris and I	_____	(talk)	_____
6.	Sarah	_____	(live)	_____
7.	stove	_____	(heat)	_____
8.	wheels	_____	(turn)	_____
9.	brother	_____	(play)	_____
10.	the four of us	_____	(wait)	_____
11.	that girl	_____	(need)	_____
12.	police officer	_____	(stop)	_____
13.	picture	_____	(hang)	_____
14.	Joe, Ann and I	_____	(dance)	_____

Exercise 2

In each sentence, fill in the bracket above the subject noun with the appropriate pronoun; then fill in the blank with the correct present-tense form of the given verb.

Example: [He]
             John *drinks* wine with every meal.   (DRINK)

_____

      [   ]
1. My plant _____ lots of sunlight here.   (GET)

      [   ]
2. Mrs. Johnson _____ on buying the tickets.   (INSIST)

        [   ]
3. Most Americans _____ television every day.   (WATCH)

      [   ]
4. My son and I _____ the neighbors who moved.   (MISS)

    [   ]
5. Bob _____ his job difficult.   (FIND)

      [   ]
6. The flowers _____ droopy.   (LOOK)

     [   ]
7. Sally _____ her two dogs daily.   (WALK)

       [   ]
8. That fact _____ me.   (CONFUSE)

    [   ]
9. Mary and I _____ Tom Selleck.   (LOVE)

    [   ]
10. Mr. Martin _____ the chalk every time he writes on the board.   (BREAK)

Exercise 3

Fill in the appropriate present-tense form of the given verb.

Remember: 1)   If the subject is *singular* (can be replaced by *he, she,* or *it*), the verb has an -*s* or -*es ending.*

2)   If the subject is *plural* (or *I* or *you*), then the present tense verb has *no ending.*

---

1. DROP   He _____ the children off at school every day.

2. WANT   Most people _____ to be honest.

3. SAY   I always _____ what I think.

4. RUN   Every morning, she _____ four miles.

5. ENJOY   Most of the time, I _____ my work.

6. SAY   All of the newspapers _____ there will be a fuel shortage.

7. SEEM   Sometimes it _____ impossible to leave.

8. HOPE   My younger sister _____ to become a teacher of deaf children.

9. TAKE   A medical career _____ a lot of training.

10. SAY   That sign _____ that the store will open at noon.

11. SEE   We usually _____ our parents once a month.

12. SEEM   New styles often _____ strange at first.

13. ASK   My teacher _____ us to do homework every weekend.

14. DO   Whatever you _____, please invite me along.

15. MARRY If she _____ him, will they stop fighting?

16. FRY   Ginger always _____ eggs until they are hard as rocks.

17. TRUST Intelligent parents _____ their children, but also keep an eye on them.

Exercise 4

First underline the subject. Then fill in the appropriate present-tense form of the given verb.

___

SAY   1. One of the doctors _____ she will recover.

INTEREST   2. The discoveries of this scientist _____ me.

JUDGE   3. Some of those teachers _____ you on appearances.

FRIGHTEN   4. Women with confidence _____ most men.

OPEN   5. The school in this town _____ tomorrow.

UNLOCK   6. Many of those keys _____ this door.

TWIST   7. The road through these mountains _____ dangerously.

LEAK   8. Some of these faucets _____ slightly.

PLAY   9. The trombones in this orchestra _____ out of
tune.

SEEM   10. The tax on household goods _____ unfair.

TEST   11. One of those exercises _____ your skill at
balancing.

CONFUSE   12. The instructions on this package _____ me.

DO   13. The manager of these stores _____ a good job.

LOOK   14. All of these books _____ boring.

SAY   15. The owner of the construction company _____ that
he is innocent.

LIVE   16. A strange man with seventy cats _____ way out on
the edge of town.

Exercise 5

The following sentences are all in the present tense. Correct the verb endings. Not every verb needs changing.

___

1. My class seem difficult.

2. Every year my husband surprise me on my birthday.

3. Jennifer take her children to school every morning at 8:00.

4. I think the movie sound scary.

5. Shirley live where the sun shine every day.

6. My sisters all loves chocolate ice cream.

7. They risk a fine by driving so fast.

8. The trains goes to St. Louis every day at noon.

9. Some teachers spends too much time talking.

10. They thinks all the students are listening to every word.

___

Exercise 6

The following sentences are all in the present tense. Correct the verb endings. Not every verb needs changing.

___

1. The disc-jockey play rock records and read commercials for various products.

2. In the morning Gretchen exercises and in the afternoon she sing.

3. That television announcer speaks with a Texas accent but his assistant speak with a New York accent.

4. That character wear the strangest costumes on Halloween.

5. My roommate listen to the radio all the time, even when she study.

6. Antiques has gone up in value during the last ten years.

7. My apartment rent for twice as much this year even though the landlord never bother fixing anything.

8. The building near the railroad tracks need lots of repairs.

9. Bob lose control of his car when he have too much to drink.

10. Your idea makes me want to jump up and down.

Exercise 7

1. Underline each verb in this paragraph.

2. Rewrite the paragraph, changing "Andy and Oscar" to "Oscar," and making whatever changes are necessary.

3. Underline every change. The first sentence will begin like this: After leaving Chicago, <u>Oscar now lives</u> on . . . .

After leaving Chicago, Andy and Oscar now live on a farm because they want a quiet life in the fresh air. They get up every morning at dawn and before breakfast pick their way through the cow dung, open the smelly chicken coop, and hold their noses as they snatch an egg. While making a fire in their woodburning stove, they choke on the smoke. Then Andy and Oscar drive a deafening tractor out to the field where, as they fill their lungs with the blowing dust, they sneeze furiously. Until late in the evening, they do chores in the barn. Exhausted, they fall asleep and dream of a sound-proof office and an air-conditioned room.

SUBJECT-VERB AGREEMENT A

Post-Test

Read the following paragraph and correct any present-tense verb ending errors.

    My sister live on the ground floor of a two-story apartment building and hates living there. For one thing, the cats in the neighborhood howl right below her bedroom window all night and knocks over her garbage cans. One cat waits patiently outside her door until she open it and then pounce on her foot, ruining her stockings. But the people living upstairs are even worse than the cats. The mother starts a fire almost every month because she forget to turn off the stove when she leave the kitchen, and the daughter faithfully practices her gymnastics every evening just as my sister sit down to study. Even more annoying, the father parks his car in my sister's parking space and peek in every time he go past her front window. All in all, living there has not been a pleasant experience for my poor sister.

V. OTHER KINDS OF AGREEMENT

SUBJECT-VERB AGREEMENT B

In the last unit, we looked at the common error of leaving off the -s ending with *he-she-it* subjects in the present tense; this is called an *agreement* error.

Many other types of agreement problems exist; in this unit we will look at a few of them.

The following is a list of common words that, when used as subjects, are singular and in the same class as *he-she-it* subjects.

each	anything	everybody
either	someone	everything
neither	somebody	no one
another	something	nobody
anyone	one	nothing
anybody	everyone	

So a sentence like:

> Everybody take a turn doing the dishes.

is not correct. It should be:

> Everybody *takes* a turn doing the dishes.

There is, are

Look at the following sentence:

> There are four apples on the table.

If the verb is *are*, how do we find the subject? Ask yourself *who* or *what* are (on the table)? You will come up with *apples* as a subject, and this is correct.

The problem with this kind of sentence is that a writer frequently begins a sentence with "There is" (or "There was"), which is singular, and follows it with a plural subject.

> There is four apples on the table.

Even though the subject comes after the verb in this type of sentence, the subject and verb must still agree.

Separated subject and verb

Sometimes when we write a sentence in which a subject and verb are separated by several words, we lose track of the subject and make the verb agree with something else in the sentence:

One of the main problems are student fees.

One is the subject of the sentence (the subject can never be in a prepositional phrase like *of the main problems*). We all know that in order to agree, the subject/verb unit should be *One is*, but why does a writer make a mistake like this? It's simple: He hasn't looked back far enough in the sentence. If he reread only part of the sentence, he might have seen this:

. . . the main *problems are* student fees.

These words do "agree." But if the writer had read the *whole* sentence again, he would have spotted the real subject.

MAN HING MARKET — CLEMENT

Exercise 1

In each of the following sentences, identify the verb and the subject, and correct agreement where necessary. (Remember that the subject will not be found within a prepositional phrase.)

---

1. I think the commercials on television is stupid.

2. There is four main problems with my job.

3. Each of you students have the power to change your life.

4. One of the reasons are his parents' wealth.

5. My paper on the governments of three countries were very interesting.

6. In her family there was two brothers and a sister.

7. The new rules and regulations of the university was very confusing.

8. The representatives of the student council values the input they get from other students.

9. The management style of many companies have an effect on the prices consumers pay.

10. Everyone has different beliefs, value different things, and hold different ideas.

In the first part of this section, we noted a list of common words that, when used as subjects, are singular. Here's one example:

Each book is available at a low cost.

In this example, *each* is singular because it means *each and every one*.

Several, few, both, and *many* are four plural words often used as subjects. Notice that when you begin a sentence with one of these words, what often follows is a cluster of words beginning with a preposition:

Several (of the *programs*) were westerns.
Few (of the *players*) are willing to take a salary cut.
Many (of the *students*) have given up their jobs.
Both (of my *brothers*) have degrees in engineering.

Each subject word above is followed by a prepositional phrase that includes an italicized plural noun. We know that the subject of the sentence is not in the prepositional phrase. But these four words aren't likely to cause agreement problems, since the subjects and the noun that follow in the prepositional phrases are both plural.

What gets confusing for most people is when the subject of the sentence and the noun that follows it in the prepositional phrase are not BOTH singular or plural.

One of the

One (of the *problems*) is too difficult for me.

One of means *one of more than one* — one of several. We use the prepositional phrase *of the* to indicate the plural group we are singling *one* out of, so a plural noun (like *problems*) always appears after *one of the*. BUT that doesn't make *problems* the subject of the sentence. ONE is still the subject, so it takes a singular verb.

Exercise 2

Follow each *one* with an *of the* prepositional phrase and verb to complete the second sentence in each pair of sentences.

---

1. My aunt always loses fifty dollars gambling in Reno.

    One of _____ fifty dollars gambling in Reno last weekend.

2. My brother goes to college in Colorado.

    One of _____ to college in Colorado.

3. Biology is the most difficult course I am taking.

    One of _____ the most difficult course I am taking.

Some of the/all of the

Some of and *all of* are tricky because they can come before both singular and plural nouns. You do need to look at the prepositional phrase to determine if the noun there is singular or plural. Be sure to read the section on count and non-count nouns if you have problems.

>   All (of the *information*) is useful.

We use the singular verb *is* in this sentence because *all of* is followed by *information*, a *singular* noun. *All* may sound like a lot, but *information* is the important word here, and no matter how much information you have, it is still a singular word.

>   Some (of the *players*) are retiring.

Here we use the plural verb *are* because *some of* is followed by the plural noun *players*.

Exercise 3

Complete each sentence by first deciding if the noun in the prepositional phrase is singular or plural, and then choosing a singular or plural verb.

1. Some of the advice _____ .

2. All of the students _____ .

3. Some of the people _____ .

4. All of my homework _____ .

Exercise 4

Here is a passage written in the singular, using *one of*. Rewrite the passage, changing *one of* to *all of* or *some of*, making the necessary verb changes as well.

One of Alex's coworkers is giving him a headache. Their supervisor hasn't noticed that one of the clerks wastes time complaining about the work load, making it impossible for Alex to get any work done. Ever since Alex got a promotion, another one of the clerks has come over to his desk during her coffee breaks to discuss the company policies, and look for ways to impress him. One of the company's more frustrated workers told him a story about his pay check bouncing three times in the same week. Alex thinks that one of these problems ought to be reported to the unit manager.

Exercise 5

Identify and correct any errors you find in the following sentences.

___

1. One of the difficulty is that he has no car.

2. She is the kind of person who has lots of friend.

3. A mountain of pressures are upon him.

4. The problems that he faces — for instance, his schedule at work — is giving him nightmares.

5. Don't forget to take one of the college aptitude test when you're supposed to.

6. There is four ways in which San Francisco is different from Los Angeles.

7. Whenever I have a blood test, goosepimple start forming on my arms.

8. In my church choir the age of singers range from fifteen to sixty.

9. Nobody in this room have to leave early.

SUBJECT-VERB AGREEMENT WITH ADJECTIVE CLAUSES

The words WHO, WHOM, WHICH, THAT, WHEN, and WHERE are often the first words of what we call adjective clauses. Like adjectives, adjective clauses modify nouns.

* When a sentence contains an adjective clause, the verb in the adjective clause usually agrees with the noun the clause modifies.

For instance:

Reading, which is my favorite activity, has helped me to do well in college and gives me a pleasurable escape when I need one.

What word does *which* refer to?

I enjoy having friends like Rosa *who come from different cultures than my own.*

What word does *who* refer to?

Exercise 6

Underline the adjective clause in each sentence once and then double-underline the noun being modified. Circle the correct verb form—the one that agrees with the noun being modified.

1. My friends who (lives/live) in Daly City just bought a house.

2. The students in the front row who (is/are) always cracking jokes keep the rest of the class laughing.

3. The tourists I met at Coit Tower, who (was/were) dressed mostly in plaid, wanted to see a real hippie.

4. The restaurant down by the docks, which (serves/serve) great seafood, is closed Sundays.

5. My dogs are the only ones in the neighborhood who (does/do) not bark at the moon.

6. Matilda is a health food nut who (detests/detest) artificial sweeteners, food coloring and preservatives.

7. Tennis is a game which (requires/require) the right equipment as well as good eye-hand coordination and stamina.

8. My car is one of those automobiles whose only saving grace (is/are) that it is paid for.

9. My best friend, who (works/work) at a movie theater, eats hot buttered popcorn, hot dogs and ice cream bon bons all night.

10. The men who (guides/guide) the tour are friendly and helpful.

Exercise 7

Are the verb forms in the following sentences correct? If not, make the appropriate corrections.

---

1. Sarah is the only one of the players who hit home runs.

2. The mailwoman gave me my mail, which, unfortunately, were mostly bills.

3. People who says writing ability isn't important are kidding themselves.

4. I find it difficult to have patience with people who like to have their own way all the time.

5. The paintings near the snack bar, which depicts local tourist attractions, bored me.

6. In order to keep up with current events which influences our lives, we should read a newspaper or watch the news regularly.

7. Most people who live by themselves appreciate a home-cooked meal.

8. My favorite restaurants are hole-in-the-wall establishments run by families who treat their customers like friends and serves reasonably-priced nutritious meals.

9. The typical American who live in the South speak more slowly than his northern counterpart.

Exercise 8

The following passage contains some common agreement errors. Find and correct the errors.

One of the biggest problem that I experience each semester are picking my classes, but after a few confusing days I usually manage to figure out a schedule. It's just that there is so many interesting classes to choose from that I end up with a long list of choices which I narrow down by looking at the days and times they are offered. I never take classes that is offered in the late afternoon or evening since I have a job which require me to work from 4:00 to 9:00 every night. I also try to choose classes taught by instructors who my friend say are enthusiastic teachers who likes their students; I know that I will learn best in a class with a good teacher. I also have several other considerations when making up my schedule. For example, many of my friend want to take classes together but I don't always like the classes they've chosen. I also have problems figuring out which classes fulfill G.E. requirements because there is so many rules to follow. Putting a class schedule together can be very frustrating, but once I have one figured out, I feel great because I know that I've arranged a workable schedule to get me through another semester of school, bringing me closer to my dream: graduation.

AGREEMENT

Post-Test

The following passage contains some common agreement errors. Find and correct the errors.

There is some very important decisions that everyone have to make while a student; one is the choice of major. Long ago I thought of majoring either in computers or clinical science or both, because both of these field interests me, both are useful, and medical technology have many job openings. Actually, I would like to work in a hospital mainly for the satisfaction of helping people, but working with computers offer a lot of possibilities, too. Now that so many different kinds of computers are being made, they are becoming more and more useful. And because the price of computers are going down, more and more hospitals can afford them, which mean more and more potential job openings. Every doctor I know, whether a specialist or general practitioner, are using computers for many purposes, and medical technologists who works with them also uses computers for research. Each of these fields offer high starting salaries. All in all, I could do well in either field, but ideally I would like to work in a hospital that use computers frequently.

VI. PRONOUN AGREEMENT

PRONOUN/ANTECEDENT AGREEMENT

We replace specific nouns with pronouns to avoid repetition. Without pronouns, some of our sentences might look like this:

> When I had lunch with Roger, Roger told me about Roger's geology class and where Roger's geology class was going on Roger's geology class' field trip.

Using pronouns, we make the sentence less wordy but maintain its clarity:

> When I had lunch with Roger *he* told me about *his* geology class and where *it* was going on *its* field trip.

The more specific noun (or noun phrase) that a pronoun replaces is called the *antecedent*. In the sentence above, for instance, the antecedent of the pronoun *he* is *Roger*, and the antecedent of the pronoun *his* is *Roger's*.

As a subject must agree with its verb, a pronoun must agree with its antecedent. In informal speech a sentence like the following is acceptable:

> When a photographer shoots a portrait session, they must try to make the subject appear natural.

But in formal writing, the sentence is incorrect, because *photographer* is singular and *they* is plural. Traditionally, when a singular pronoun is called for and the sex of the person referred to is not known, we have used *he, him,* or *his*.

> When a photographer shoots a portrait session, *he* must try to make the subject appear natural.

But the language is changing in this area; many feel that the automatic use of *he* excludes women, that the sentence above, for example, might suggest that all photographers are male.

We have other options to make our pronouns agree. We can include both sexes:

> When a photographer shoots a portrait session, *he or she* must try to make *his or her* subject appear natural, so that *he or she* can be assured of *his or her* client's satisfaction.

But many readers also find this method wordy. One other option, when it makes sense in the context of our writing, is to make the pronoun and its antecedent plural:

> When photographers shoot portrait sessions, they must try to make the subjects appear natural.

Exercise 1

Change the following sentences so that the pronouns agree.

---

1. A good many people have a 9 to 5 job and work very hard at them.

2. If a person is going to commit a crime, they should be prepared to face the consequences.

3. I enjoy playing many sports, but I also like watching it on television.

4. Even though the average student tries to use their time wisely, they often fall prey to the many distractions of college life.

5. Each of my brothers has their own car.

6. Someone called late last night, but they hung up when I answered the phone.

7. Most of the time when a customer doesn't try a dress on first, they will only have to return it later.

SHIFT IN PERSON

Pronouns can be divided into three groups:

1. The *first person* is who is *speaking*:

    I/me   we/us

2. The *second person* is who is being *spoken to:*

    you

3. The *third person* is who is being *spoken about*:

    she/her   he/him   one   they/them

Now look at the following example:

When *one* is tired and under stress, *your* productivity declines.

Though in the example above the pronouns may both be singular, *one* and *your* don't refer to the same "person." The sentence can be corrected in any of the following ways:

When *you* are tired and under stress, *your* productivity declines.

When *one* is tired and under stress, *his* or *her* productivity declines.

When *people* are tired and under stress, *their* productivity declines.

*   NOTE: In writing, we usually avoid "you," using it only when we are actually writing directly to the reader as an individual. If you mean "many people" or "most people" or even "everybody," use third person pronouns. If you really mean "I," say "I."

Exercise 2

Correct the following sentences so that pronouns agree.

_____

1. When one is very young, you often don't understand the pressures that parents face.

2. I liked the movie because it kept you on the edge of your seat.

3. Professor Clark told us that we don't have to answer the last essay question unless you want to skip one of the first four.

4. Either one can seek learning experiences or they can live for their possessions.

5. When you go shopping, one should have a specific list.

Exercise 3

Rewrite the following sentences so that the reference of the underlined pronoun is clear.

1. Roger removed the engine from his car before he sold <u>it</u>.

2. Before <u>she</u> was chosen as president, Martha and Yvette had been close friends.

3. When I pulled the car into the gas station, <u>it</u> was empty.

4. Ed told his father that <u>he</u> would have to pay for the ticket.

5. Cynthia has decided to go on a trip to the Sierra. She has never been backpacking but intends to buy <u>one</u>.

AQUATIC PARK — FOOT OF HYDE STREET

VII. THE -ED ENDING ON VERBS

PAST-TENSE VERB ENDINGS

The following passage is in the past tense. Underline the verb in each sentence, then the subject.

Last year Sherry lived at home and commuted to school. Because of the bus situation, she sometimes arrived late for classes, and missed the beginning of several lectures. This annoyed her very much. Also, she often wanted to stay at school in the evening for movies and concerts, but her parents refused. They worried about her being on the bus after dark. Sherry's parents also showed their protectiveness in many other ways. They allowed her dates only with boys from church or from their neighborhood.

Sherry rebelled against these conditions during her sophomore year. Without the knowledge or permission of her parents, Sherry applied for a job at a Stonestown store, and she landed a position in the cosmetics department of a small department store. She rented a room near campus for $120 a month, but since the landlady failed to provide cooking facilities, Sherry ended up spending a lot of money in restaurants for every meal. Sherry's mother and father disapproved of her moving out, but they agreed to let Sherry go. Sherry escaped from her parents, but she worked such long hours to pay for her room and meals that she never found the time to go to a movie or concert.

1. Find three combinations of singular subjects (I-you-he-she-it) and verbs (example: *Sherry lived*) and write them here:

2. Find three combinations of plural subjects (we-they-you) and verbs (example: *they agreed*) and write them here:

3. Is there any difference in past tense verb endings between the singular and the plural? _____ What do they have in common?

4. What is the rule for forming the past tense of verbs?

    *   NOTE: This rule applies to verbs that have only one form in the past tense, such as *learn-learned-(have) learned*. It does not apply to verbs with two forms in past tense such as *sing-sang-(have) sung* or *do-did-(have) done*. Use your dictionary if you don't know a verb's past tense forms.

        ALERT: *supposed to* and *used to* always have an -ed ending!

        She was suppose*d* to show her identification.

        They use*d* to go dancing every Friday night.

        I am suppose*d* to be home in an hour.

        He is use*d* to taking a walk after dinner.

        He use*d* to walk five miles each evening.

Exercise 1

Fill in the blank with the correct past tense form of the verb given.

FRY   1.   We _____ the fish we caught over the open fire.

STUDY   2.   All of us _____ hard for the chemistry exam.

CRY   3.   Mary _____ on his shoulder all through the movie.

MARRY   4.   She _____ him on Saturday and left him the following Monday.

TRY   5.   Although the tickets were sold out weeks in advance, John _____ to get in the concert by posing as a photographer.

SHOP   6.   Anthony _____ for all his Christmas presents at the art fair last summer.

ADMIT   7.   No one _____ that he was tired.

PLAN   8.   Nancy and Jim _____ their divorce as if they were going on vacation.

TERRIFY   9.   The fireworks _____ the smaller children.

COMPILE   10.   The teachers _____ the many materials into an effective handbook.

Exercise 2

Rewrite the following sentences, changing the verb from present to past tense.

---

1. Jane likes John.

2. Marie looks terrific in her yellow dress.

3. My grandparents live in San Jose.

4. The monkey always asks for attention.

5. Lucy plays tennis more often than Fred.

6. After a victory, he holds his head high.

7. Her dog howls by the light of the moon.

8. Sam donates every spare cent to the San Francisco Zoo.

9. The young couple announces their wedding plans to their parents.

10. The dog growls at salesmen, but he never snarls at Avon ladies.

58

Exercise 3

In each of the following sentences, underline any words that should have an "-ed" or "-d" ending and supply the missing letters.

---

1. The elephant ask Mary for a ride.

2. Fred use to live in Berkeley.

3. Jane studied all night and so she pass the exam.

4. College students are suppose to attend every class meeting.

5. All night long, Laura listen to the beat of the drums.

6. Until I started school, I work fifty hours a week.

7. Finally the cat return home.

8. As soon as the cat returned, our dog, who is suppose to be man's best friend, disappear for three weeks.

9. I'm afraid because of a crime I witness some years ago.

10. She serve us tacos for dinner, but she realize too late that she fail to pick up a can of refried beans when she shop for groceries last week.

SPECIAL PATTERNS

Be, Have, Get plus Main Verb

Pattern 1   Verb forms following "be," "have," and "get."

Some verb forms have two parts, first a form of "to be," "to have," or "to get," and then a main verb. In these verb forms, the main verb always has an "-ed" or "-en" ending (the past participle) — no matter what form of the helping verb you use.

1.   In my favorite restaurant, the meals *are served* quickly and courteously.

2.   Last year an award *was given* to the restaurant, and the chef *was thrilled* when his innovative recipes won the award.

3.   The restaurant *has* always *drawn* tourists from all over the country.

4.   Laura *has worked* as a waitress at this restaurant for a couple of years.

5.   She *got bored* with her previous job as a secretary.

6.   Now she *gets tipped* very well for her work.

Remember: In each of these sentences, the time of the action—the tense—is shown by the form of "to be," "to have," or "to get" that you use (the helping verb). The main verb always has a past participle ending: "are serve*d*," and "was give*n*," for example.

Proofreading Tip

If you have a problem with "-ed" or "-en" endings, go through your essay and underline any forms of *be* (is, are, was, were, be, been, being), and forms of *have* (has, have, had, having) and *get* (get, got). Are any of them *followed* by another verb form? If so, does the main verb—the verb form that comes after *be, have,* or *get*—need an "-ed" or "-en" ending?

Exercise 4

Find words in the following sentences which need "-d" or "-ed" endings and fill in the missing letters. Some sentences may be correct.

---

1. I am always bore by the lectures in my economics class.

2. A whole family of mice has occupy my kitchen.

3. Many adults are prejudice against the music their children

    listen to.

4. The city's plan to build a new baseball stadium has backfire.

5. Rock singers are often stereotype as stupid and rebellious.

6. In my role as a student, I try to be well-prepare for classes,

    quizzes, and tests.

7. In his new apartment, Jim won't be disturb by the neighbors

    because the ceilings have been soundproof.

Pattern 2   Adjectives formed from verbs

Some words with "-ed" endings actually work like adjectives, and modify nouns. In the sentence

> The chef tossed the salad

the verb in the sentence is *tossed*. The same word may also be used as an adjective.

> We enjoyed the *tossed* salad at a dinner last night.

*   These adjectives formed from verbs normally keep their "-ed" endings, like the following examples:

   To graduate, you must take many require*d* courses.

   The feature*d* performers arrived so late that the audience was restless.

Adjectives formed from verbs may come before the nouns they modify:

The *assigned* textbooks cost $35.38.

Or they may follow the noun they modify:

The exercises *assigned* by the instructor were due on Monday.

*   In the two patterns that follow, the verb form *never* takes an "-ed" ending:

1.   If the verb *immediately* follows the word "to."

Incorrect:	We wanted *to crowned* him king.
Correct:	We want *to crown* him king.

2.   If the verb form comes immediately after one of the special helping verbs below.

can	may	must
could	might	do/does/did
will	shall	
would	should	

Incorrect:	*Did* he *learned* the information for the test?
Correct:	*Did* he *learn* the information for the test?

Incorrect:	We *can walked* to the movie theatre.
Correct:	We *can walk* to the movie theatre.

NOTE: If some form of "be" or "have" *follows* one of these helping verbs, the main verb form will take the "-ed/-en" ending (see Pattern 1, p. 59). For example:

The letter *could* not *be answered* right away.

In December, Rosa *will have worked* here for two years.

I would like *to have been* at the party last night.

Exercise 5

Find all the words in the following sentences which need "-d" or "-ed" endings and fill in the missing letters.

___

1. Many of the sale items were purchase quickly by the numerous customers.

2. Student fees were raise this semester, and many irritated student have protest to the administration.

3. The room was examine for clues, but the frighten witnesses refused to help the detective in his efforts to solve the crime.

4. Twenty-five points were score by the visiting team by the end of the second quarter, and the frustrate fans of the home team knew that the victory would not be theirs.

5. The SPCA has express concern about the large number of abandon pets, and they furthermore have claimed that the number of pets who are abuse by their owners is on the rise as well.

6. The flight delay had occur because of poor weather conditions, but after a few hours the plane took off.

7. The tests have to be score by hand, so the teacher is upset because he wants them to be return tomorrow.

8. It had not occur to the fireman that the abandon building would be occupied.

63

PAST TENSE VERB FORMS

Post-Test

Proofread the following passage for correct use of words ending in " d" or "-ed."

Last week Tom and his wife witness a horrible robbery. As they were walking along the street one evening, they pass a darken alley. When Tom pause to glance into the alleyway, he notice that a man had been push up against a wall of a building. Another man stood in front of him holding a load gun. Tom watch as the terrify victim hand over his wallet fill with credit cards, pieces of identification, and some cash. Tom's wife turn to see what he was looking at, and she suddenly scream. The robber turn, quickly stuff the wallet into the pocket of his coat, then fire at them with the gun, but fortunately miss them. The frighten couple ran to help the robbery victim. The man's face was flush with fright; still, they were glad to discover that he was basically unharm. A reward has been offer for the capture of the robber. Tom and his wife were ask by the police to give as much information as they could, but since it had been so dark, their description of the robber was plague with a lot of non-specific information. So the police haven't caught the robber yet.

PROOFREADING FOR VERB ERRORS

A. To avoid inappropriate *tense shifts* . . .

        Step 1.   In each clause of the essay, underline the verb—the word that shows the t time-frame of the clause.

        Step 2.   Now go back to the beginning of the essay and highlight every place where you have shifted from one time-frame to another (for example, from past to present, present to past, past to future).

        Step 3 .   In each place where this happens, ask yourself, "Does the meaning of this statement justify the change in time-frame?" To make this decision, read a few sentences before the one you're working on, and a few that follow it; they create the context of the sentence. Then decide whether the tense-shift makes sense.

        NOTE: This process will also help you spot places where you need past-tense endings on verbs.

B. To clear up "-*ed*" or "-*en*" problems . . .

        Step 1.   Go through your essay and underline any forms of *be, have,* and *get.*

        Step 2.   Check to see if any of them are followed by a main verb (you may find a modifier between the helping verb and the main verb, so look carefully at what you've written).

        Step 3.   Add "-ed" or "-en" endings as appropriate to the main verbs.

C. To check *subject-verb agreement* . . .

        Step 1.   In each clause of the essay, underline the verb—just as in the process for checking tense-shifts—if you haven't already done so.

        Step 2.   Identify and underline the subject of every verb (if you've forgotten how to find subjects, review "Locating Subjects," on p. 3).

        Step 3.   Remember that verbs that end in "s" are always third-person singular. The subject for an "s"-ending verb must be singular. If a verb does not have singular form, the subject must be plural (or compound: "Scott and David drive to school every day").

        NOTE: Use the content of your sentence—your meaning—to decide whether you need or want singular or plural forms for the subject and verb.

VIII. SPECIAL TENSES

THE PAST-TO-PRESENT TENSE (present Perfect Tense)

The past-to-present (present perfect) tense has *three* forms:

1. has/have + -ed (past participle)

    Frank *has moved* into a new apartment.

    My brothers *have liked* science-fiction movies since they were children.

    I *have* already *seen* that movie. (irregular verb past participle)

2. has/have + been + -ed (past participle)

    The library *has been closed* since noon.

    They *have been cheated* by their landlord once too often.

3. has/have + been + -ing

    Ever since I insulted her, she *has been avoiding* me.

    Professor Carlson *has been teaching* at this university for twenty-two years.

The past-to-present tense has *two uses:*

1. It is used for a situation that began in the past but continues into the present.

    He *has worked* at St. Mary's Hospital for five years. (He still works there.)

    If the situation no longer exists, use the simple past.

    He *worked* at St. Mary's Hospital for five years. (He no longer works there.)

*   Whenever you use *since + a particular time*, you have to use the past-to-present.

    My brother *has been playing* the piano *since he was five years old.*
    The university *has been closed since Friday.*

    I *have felt* much better *since I went to see Mr. Mayers.*

2. The past-to-present is also used for something that happened at an *unspecified* time in the past.

    He *has often* visited Mexico. (Do we know exactly when?)

    I *have seen* that movie seven times. (Do we know exactly when?)

*   If a specific time is mentioned, use the simple past:

    He *visited* Mexico last summer.

    I *saw* that movie again last night.

Exercise 1

Examine the sentences presented in the section on the *forms* of the past-to-present and decide, in each case, why the past-to-present was used. If it was used for a situation that began in the past but continues into the present, mark *1*. If it was used to indicate that something happened at an unspecified time in the past, mark *2*.

_____ 1. Frank has moved into a new apartment.

_____ 2. My brothers have liked science-fiction movies since they were children.

_____ 3. I have already seen the movie.

_____ 4. The library has been closed since noon.

_____ 5. They have been cheated by their landlord once too often.

_____ 6. Ever since I insulted her, she has been avoiding me.

_____ 7. Professor Carlson has been teaching at this university for twenty-two years.

Exercise 2

Use either the past-to-present or the simple past as needed.

_____

1. I (go) _____ to a party at Tony's last night.

2. I (attend) _____ many parties since I began college.

3. Frank (arrive) _____ here three days ago.

4. Bill (be) _____ here since last Tuesday.

5. Try not to be absent from class again for the rest of the term.
   You (miss, already) _____ too many classes. You (miss)
   _____ two classes just last week.

6. Recently, medical researchers around the world (do) _____ a
   great deal of research on AIDS.

7. The mass media (affect) _____ the values and beliefs of
   people all over the world.

8. Yesterday in my psychology class, I (learn) _____ why some
   people are afraid of being in a small crowded space.

9. I (discover) _____ that if I budget my time carefully, I
   can get all of my work done and still have some free time left
   over.

10. When I was working on my last essay, I (discover) _____
    that my favorite time to write is early in the morning.

Exercise 3

The writer of this paragraph wrote it mostly in the past tense, but many of the verbs should be in the past-to-present tense. Change the verbs that are inappropriate in the past tense to the past-to-present tense. (Do *not* change present-tense verbs.)

Recently the UCSF Medical Center has opened two new clinics. One, the Refugee Screening Clinic at San Francisco General Hospital, treats recent immigrants from all over the world. It rapidly found that its biggest problem is communication. Over time it solved the problem by locating translators fluent in languages as diverse as Cambodian, Polish, Tigrigna, and Farsi, and trained them to explain complicated medical procedures and technology to the patients. It discovered that the translators can also help them understand the personal and

cultural backgrounds of the patients, whether they came from Southeast Asia, Eastern Europe, Africa, or the Middle East. Some of the patients have traditional or cultural beliefs different from those of modern medicine. For instance, while many people now consider blood tests a normal part of a visit to the doctor, many others believed all their lives that when a little blood is drawn, the body's natural balance is upset. Some take medications or herbs that were traditional in their cultures for centuries, and doctors must be sure they do not prescribe medications that conflict with them. For the staff as well as the patients, the clinic provided an important experience in health care.

THE PAST-BEFORE-PAST TENSE (Past Perfect Tense)

Like the past-to-present, the past-before-past (past perfect) tense also has *three* forms:

1. had + -*ed* (past participle) — had arrived, had fallen

2. had + been + -*ed* (past participle) — had been removed

3. had + been + -*ing* — had been singing

The past-before-past tense is used to indicate that something happened *before* something else happened *when both things happened in the past.*

By the time you arrived, *I had left.* (Which happened first?)

The thief simply walked in because someone *had forgotten* to lock the door. (Which happened first?)

Her eyes were red because she *had been crying* (Which happened first?)

Until yesterday, I *had* never *heard* about it. (This is tricky. Something is missing—but understood. What happened yesterday? What happened *before* yesterday?)

*   When *before* or *after* is used to make the time relationship clear, the use of the past-before-past is optional; the simple past may be used as well:

    I *had left* before you arrived.
    I *left* before you arrived.

    I left after you *had arrived.*
    I left after you *arrived.*

*   When writing about an incident that happened in the past, be careful to use the past-before-past *only when necessary:*

    As I *walked* down the lonely street at midnight, I *thought* I *heard* footsteps behind me. The footsteps *grew* louder and louder. I suddenly *stopped* and *whirled* around to face whoever *was following* me. But no one *was* there. My imagination *had been playing* tricks on me.

    > Only the verb in the final sentence is in the past-before-past tense because only in this sentence does the writer refer to something (his imagination playing tricks on him) that happened at an earlier point in the narrative (before he turned around and discovered no one was there).

Which verb in the following sentence should be changed to the past-before-past tense?

The following day when I told my friend what happened he just shook his head and smiled.

70

Exercise 1

Use the past-before-past or the simple past as needed. Read each sentence carefully before you change verbs. Are there some places where either tense is possible?

_____

1. Dinosaurs (became) _____ extinct by the time the first

   humans (appear) _____ on the earth.

2. Yesterday I (see) _____ Susan Chan, an old friend whom I

   (see, not) _____ in years. At first I (recognize, not)

   _____ her because she (gain) _____ fifty pounds.

3. Joe suddenly (realize) _____ that the teacher (ask)

   _____ him a question.

4. She (be) _____ a teacher before she (became) _____ a

   lawyer.

5. It (be) _____ midnight. I (study) _____ for five

   straight hours.

6. I (feel) _____ a little better after I (take) _____

   the medicine.

7. The movie (begin, already) _____ by the time I (arrive)

   _____ at the theatre.

8. When I (go) _____ to see my math teacher about why I

   (receive) _____ a failing grade on the last test, he

   (examine) _____ my paper, then (announce) _____ that

   he (make) _____ a mistake and (change) _____ my grade

   to an "A."

9. When I (try) _____ to explain to my friend why I (call,

   not)_____ him in several weeks, he (tell) _____ me not

   to worry because he (be) _____ out of town for a month.

Exercise 2

Much of the following paragraph is written in the past tense. Many of the verbs would be more appropriate in the past-before-past form. Change the ones that should be changed into past-before-past.

Each of us can think of annoying or embarrassing experiences we have had. One in particular comes to mind when I am daydreaming about the past. It occurred on the Tuesday before Thanksgiving in 1980; I just finished doing the dishes and was ready to take the garbage out. Wrapping it securely and walking downstairs, I suddenly felt something underfoot and heard a snapping noise. A second later my feet slipped and I found myself sitting on the stairs. It got dark early so I couldn't see very well, but I finally spotted what I stepped on: it was a very small, hard pine cone. I was so angry that I threw it thirty feet into the neighbor's yard. Then I picked up the garbage and put it in the trash can, limped upstairs, and examined my foot. It already got red and slightly swollen. When I went to the doctor the next day, he took an X-ray, examined it and announced I broke my foot. When I told him what happened, he laughed out loud, then sent me to have a cast put on. I never wore a cast or used crutches before that, but I learned how to get around quite efficiently. Ever since, then, I have a healthy respect for the power of the pine cone.

Exercise 3

In each of the following sentences, choose the correct verb form. Be prepared to explain why you made the choices you did.

---

1. Interest in making English the official language of the United States (increase) _____ recently.

2. When the Surgeon General's report (come) _____ out warning people of the danger of smoking, millions of Americans (quit) _____ even though they (smoke) _____ regularly.

3. Magazines such as *Good Housekeeping* and *Family Circle* (be) _____ popular from the time they first (appear) _____ on the market.

4. By the time I (reach) _____ my thirteenth birthday five years ago, I (spend) _____ thousands of hours watching television.

5. When Frank (look) _____ in the mirror, he suddenly (realize)_____ how much weight he (gain) _____.

6. Americans (be) _____ enthusiastic about situation comedies since the earliest days of television.

7. The widespread use of "crack" cocaine among teenagers (be) _____ a problem the government (solve, not) _____ yet.

8. Until she (become) _____ a movie star, Cybill Shepherd (be) _____ a model in New York for many years.

9. Last week Louise finally (begin) _____ to look for a new job because she (give up) _____ hope of ever being promoted in her current job.

10. In the last few years, a small number of major corporations (give) _____ a lot of attention to the problem of providing child-care facilities for their employees.

SPECIAL TENSES

Post-Test

The following paragraph is written mostly in simple present and past tenses. Many of the verbs should be either past-to-present (present perfect) or past-before-past (past perfect) forms. Make all the changes you think are appropriate.

The differences between a two-year-old and a one-year-old child are striking. "Two" has learned to do a number of things he hadn't yet mastered when he was only a year old. He found out how to grasp small objects, for instance, a Cheerio. He now successfully used utensils when eating, while a year ago, he used only his fingers to get food to his mouth. "Two" discovered how to hold a cup and tried to pour from it, spilling the contents, of course. He also built a small tower of blocks, and threw a ball, while earlier he was able only to hold the blocks or ball. And he mastered the trick of climbing stairs, while a year ago he toddled on flat surfaces. But he isn't a "Terrible Two" for no reason at all: he learned how to make trouble. He draws murals on the wall with his crayons. He got to the point where he can put two or more words together in a very loud voice, often in public places. He picked up an important vo-cabulary item, "No," and experimented with various projects like crawling underfoot in the kitchen and emptying cupboards. In other words, he became more skillful at upsetting his parents. While, at one, he simply cried in frustration, by the age of two he made tan-trums into an art form; he figured out how to stamp his feet and throw things. In short, he developed a great deal during the year between his first and second birthdays.

IX. SPECIAL HELPING VERBS

Two verbs—*would* and *could*—seem to cause problems for many of us. The problems are that

1) we use them too much,
2) we use them in sentences where they don't belong.

We have to keep track of what we mean in order to figure out when it's appropriate to use *would* or *could:* we really have to think through what we're trying to say in order to make the right decision.

Habitual Action

We often use simple present tense to show actions that are repeated or habitual.

> On warm sunny days I sit in the sun for awhile; then I water my plants, rearrange flower pots in my patio, and pull weeds, or I wash, wax, and polish my car. On gray days, I clean house.

And we often use "*would* + verb" to show actions repeated in the past. Read the following paragraph. Underline each verb or verb phrase, and try to see how some are different from others.

> Some years ago, my grandfather died, but my memories of him remain vivid to this day. He enjoyed being around small children, and would always sing to them, rocking them back and forth in an old overstuffed rocking chair. He would invent silly games, which they loved, and would come up with even sillier jokes, which made everyone under the age of six laugh. He would always help anyone who needed it—and since he was married to a woman who had seven sisters, there was always someone, somewhere, who needed help. But he never wanted the rest of the family to know that he had given money or advice in a tough situation; he liked his acts of kindness to be "secrets."

Some of these verbs are simple past tense ("enjoyed"), but some use the two-part form, "*would* + verb" without an -ed ending ("would invent").

In writing about a one-time-only action in the past (a completed action), we use the simple past tense:

> Nearly a million people *walked* across the Golden Gate Bridge.

> On my seventh birthday, my aunt *gave* me a wonderful present.

> Some years ago, my grandfather *died* . . .

In the paragraph above, though, the verbs are not all simple past tense forms; here are a few of the verbs from the paragraph:

1	2
enjoyed	would sing
loved	would invent
needed	would come up with
wanted	would help

These lists show two different kinds of verbs: the first names states of being or of feeling; the second names acts or events.

We use *would* with the second group to show that the actions named took place on a regular, habitual, or customary basis.

> He . . . would always sing [he regularly sang to them].

> He would invent silly games . . . [he had the habit of inventing silly games].

> He would always help anyone who needed it . . . [he had a custom of helping people].

These verbs in the second group, and others like them, name *actions or events that take place, stop for a while, and take place again.* They are not necessarily ongoing actions—just repeatable, and repeated.

As a general rule, when you want to show or imply that something has occurred in the past *more than once* and has occurred *regularly,* you can use "*would* + main verb" (without any tense ending on the main verb).

Also as a general rule, when you use "*would* + main verb," the verb should be the kind shown in the second group—verbs that name actions or events rather than states of being or conditions of life.

LOUIE'S & THE CLIFF HOUSE
AT SEAL ROCK

X. CONDITIONALS

"If" plus *would/could*

Look at the following sentence:

> If I am finished in time, I'll give you a call.

Let's break it down. First there's an "if" clause. "If" means "in case," "in the event that," "on condition that," "when," "whenever." In other words, in an "if" sentence, you're saying that in order for something to happen, something else must happen first. The first something is stated in the "if," or *condition*, clause.

"If" can be used in two kinds of statements: "regular" and "hypothetical."

REGULAR conditionals indicate events or actions that are *genuinely possible.*

1. If/when you drive on the freeway, you watch the traffic carefully. (We often do drive on the freeway.)

2. If/when the traffic slows down you also reduce speed. (Traffic often does slow down.)

3. If/when a driver applies the brakes slowly, he will stop more smoothly.

What is the verb tense in the "if" clause of each sentence? _____

Is the tense of the verb in each main clause the same as the others? _____

Which one is different? _____

> The "if" clauses are in _____ tense.

> The main clauses are either _____ or _____ tense.

> *   REGULAR conditionals use present tense in the "if" clause, and present *or* future in the main clause.

> **   "If" and "when" can both be used in REGULAR conditionals.

76

Exercise 1

Think of a main clause to add to each of the "if" clauses, and then write it in the space provided. Be sure to use the appropriate verb tenses.

_____

1. If Pete gets his own apartment, _____ _____

    _____.

2. If he decides to get a roommate, _____

    _____.

3. If he decides to live alone, _____

    _____.

4. When he doesn't do his laundry regularly, _____

    _____.

5. When he doesn't pay his bills on time, _____

    _____.

Next, read the following passage:

> I live in San Franciso. If I'm lucky, I can swim in the bay a few days a year. But if I lived in Hawaii, I would be able to swim in the ocean all year round. And if I had been born there, I would have spent my childhood at the beach, playing in the sand and water.

What is the one known fact stated in this paragraph? _____.

The second and third sentences in the paragraph both contain "if" clauses—but even though they look alike, they aren't. How are they different? The first one is just like the ones you've already worked on—it talks about something that's really possible: I *might* get lucky.

The second "if" clause, though, contradicts the given fact: I *don't* live in Hawaii, but in San Francisco. And so does the third: I was *not* born there.

We communicate this idea—that we are contradicting a known fact—by means of the verb form. On the lines below, answer these questions about the paragraph above:

1. In the second "if" clause, what is the form of the verb? _____ What is the form of the verb in the main clause? _____

2. How are they different from the verbs in the first "if" sentence in the paragraph?

    "If" clause _____

    Main clause _____

This second kind of conditional is called HYPOTHETICAL, or contrary-to-fact, because the "if" clause states *an improbable or unreal condition,* one that goes against the facts. And we show that we're setting up an improbable condition by using different verb forms: in writing a HYPOTHETICAL conditional, we always put the verb in some past tense form.

*   *Present* HYPOTHETICAL conditionals use past tense in the "if" clause and *would* or *could* + main verb in the main clause.

1. If I *had* wheels instead of feet, I *would be* a roller skating champion. (But I don't have wheels.)

2. If the laws of physics *didn't* work, my bed *would be* on the ceiling. (But the laws of physics do work, usually.)

3. If the state *wrote* voter information pamphlets in plain English, more of us *could understand* whom and what we're voting for.

SPECIAL NOTE: Forms of "to be" in the conditional can be tricky: In speaking, we often use "was." In writing, we normally use "were" even if the subject is singular:

If John Lennon *were* still alive, he might be making records with his son, Julian. And if Julian *were* playing in San Francisco, I would go to the concert.

Exercise 2

Following are the beginnings of several present hypothetical conditionals. The "if" clauses are correctly written in the past tense. Complete the sentences by adding a main clause to each, choosing the verb forms carefully.

---

1. If I had a lot of money, _____.

2. If I did not have to go to school,_____.

3. If the book were not full of technical terms,_____.

4. If Christmas came in July, _____.

5. If the population of my neighborhood doubled overnight,_____

    _____.

---

*   *Past* HYPOTHETICAL conditionals use past-before-past (past perfect) in the "if" clause and *would* or *could have* + main verb in the main clause. In these sentences, the verb forms look like this:

> If I *had made* more money last year, I *would have gone* on a vacation.

> > The "if" clause = *had* + main verb with "-ed/-en" ending.

> > The main clause = *would/could* + *have* + main verb with "-ed/-en" ending.

> If I *had been* more talented, I *would have been* a concert pianist.

> If the state *had written* the voter information pamphlet in plain English before the last election, more of us *could have understood* what and who we were voting for.

NOTE: Never write "would had" or "could had," as no such forms exist in English.

Exercise 3

Following are several *past time hypothetical* conditionals. Fill in the correct verb form in each of the blanks.

The Beatles — John, Paul, George, and Ringo — made revolutionary

changes in music and style. If it _____ for the Beatles,
                                        be, not

many British rockers, like the Rolling Stones, probably _____ so
                                                          become, not

popular. If the Beatles _____ the Maharishi in India, fewer
                              visit, not

Westerners in the '60's and 70's _____ about Eastern religion,
                                     know

boys _____ their hair long, and people _____ so free to
        grow, not   be, not

experiment with psychedelic drugs. The Beatles were very outspoken

and rebellious; they sometimes acted impulsively, doing things that

some people think they should not have done. If they _____ the
                                                         act, not

way they did, though, part of a social revolution _____ .
                                                    occur, not

Exercise 4

Following are several hypothetical "if" clauses. Complete the sentences by adding a main clause to each and write them out in the space provided. Be sure you select the appropriate verb form.

1. If I could do anything I wanted to do, _____ .

2. If my accounting professor were to speak more clearly, _____

    _____ .

3. If I had visited Jamaica last year, _____ .

4. If parents treated their children with respect, _____

    _____ .

5. If I were you, _____ .

Read the following short paragraph, and underline *all* verbs.

(1) I realize that a program of regular exercise would bring me a number of benefits. (2) I would improve my cardio-vascular system, (3) which can probably stand improving, (4) and I would probably get rid of some of the fat around my waist. (5) That would be a definite benefit, (6) for it does not improve my appearance, (7) and I am beginning to need new clothes that fit. (8) All in all, I would certainly do well to begin an aerobics class or start jogging three or four times a week.

Where do you see conditional verbs? Numbers _____

Do you see any "if" clauses? _____

The conditional verbs in clauses 1, 2, 4, 5, and 8 are all based on an unstated "if" idea: "If I were to begin a program of regular exercise . . . "

Sometimes we write paragraphs like this, in which the "if" idea is not stated directly, but is implied. In these paragraphs, not every verb needs to have a conditional form. For instance, the verbs in clauses 3, 6, and 7 name situations that actually exist, so the verbs are not in conditional forms.

To avoid confusing a reader about what's real and what's hypothetical, we have to select the correct verb forms.

Exercise 5

The following passages present hypothetical situations along with factual material. Change the verbs in each passage into conditional or factual verb forms as appropriate. In the space preceding each passage, write the "if" idea that lies behind the passage.

---

1. If _____ .

A victory by the South in the American Civil War would have produced historical results far different from the ones that actually took place. The South (extend) its control over the areas that are now New Mexico, Arizona, Oklahoma, and possibly even Baja California, and a second war with Mexico possibly (result). Although there (be) agreement by modern historians that slavery (be) a dying institution even in the mid-19th century, it certainly (continue) much longer than it did.   It (be) interesting to speculate on whether two relatively weak American nations (survive) into the 20th century or whether the inherently stronger North gradually (absorb) the Southern states back into a national union or (reconquer) the South by force of arms.

2. If _____ .

The results of a major earthquake in San Francisco would be devastating. It (destroy) almost all of the older large buildings, and (damage) even many of the new ones in the downtown area, for their designs (not, test) in an actual major earthquake elsewhere. Gas, electricity, and phone service (lose) for weeks in many areas, and families throughout the city (not, able) to cook meals or heat their houses. Many of these houses themselves (ruin) because they (not, bolt) to their foundations. Essential businesses such as food stores (close) for indefinite periods, and looting and other forms of lawlessness (occur) because police services (be) overextended. A catastrophic fire such as the one that (break out) during the 1906 earthquake (be) a real danger because water mains (rupture) throughout the city. In short, although most people (find) life in San Francisco as pleasant and rewarding as it is anywhere in the world, a major earthquake (make) it difficult at best.

GREEN APPLE BOOKS — CLEMENT

Exercise 6

Write a paragraph on one of the following topics. The paragraph should be at least 150 words in length.

---

1. How would school be different if you didn't have to worry about grades or so many GE requirements?

2. What would you do if you were stranded on a desert island?

3. If you could have any wish granted, what would it be, and how would your life change as a result?

XI. CAPITALIZATION

CAPITALIZATION RULES

CAPITALIZE:

1. the first word of every sentence

   The director wanted to shoot the scene all over again.

2. languages and nationalities

   Chinese
   Tagalog
   Spanish
   French
   Russian
   English
   Filipino

3. titles of specific courses . . . but not the names of specific fields unless they are also the names of languages

First Year Composition	composition
Psychology 200	psychology
Organic Chemistry II	chemistry
English 50	English

   To major in engineering, the first course one must take is Engineering 101.

   This semester I am taking engineering, biology, and Spanish.

4. names of persons, titles or abbreviated titles, and sacred names

Capitalize	Do Not Capitalize
John Smith, Ph.D.	man
Dr. Bernadette Williams	doctor
Saint Augustine	saint
President Reagan	
or the President	president
Mother (when used as a name)	my mother
Grandfather (when used as a name)	the grandfather
God	

5. names of specific places and locations (buildings, streets)

Capitalize	Do Not Capitalize
Lowell High School	high school
the Department of Humanities	department
Terrace Drive	drive
16th Street	street
Kansas	state
San Francisco State University	university
Paris, France	city, country

6. religions

Catholic
Protestant
Jewish
Buddhist
Moslem

7. specific groups, organizations, institutions, businesses

U.S. Army
Supreme Court
Republican Party
Prentice-Hall, Inc.

8. months, days, holidays . . . but not seasons

Capitalize	Do Not Capitalize
January, February, March, etc.	spring
Monday, Tuesday, etc.	summer
New Year's Day	fall
Martin Luther King's Birthday	winter

9. the first letter of words in titles of books, magazines, plays, stories, poems, movies, etc. except words like *a, an, the, and, of, in,* unless they are the first words of the title

Esquire   *Cats*
For Whom the Bell Tolls   *The Color Purple*

10. names of events or periods in history

the Renaissance
World War II

11. *north, south, east,* and *west* only when they refer to a specific geographical location

> Birds fly north in the spring.
> Are we driving east or west?
> Scott is from the Midwest while Vicky was raised in the Deep South.

Exercise 1

In the following sentences, underline words that should begin with capital letters.

---

1. many authors from the deep south have contributed greatly to american literature.

2. my roommate, whose mother never taught her about the value of money, ran up a big bill with pacific telephone.

3. during the month of december, when winter weather is at its worst, sales of sweaters and gloves increase dramatically in department stores all over the north and in the east.

4. my best friend, rosa, speaks both spanish and portuguese and eats potato chips as though they were going out of style.

5. every state in the country has a governor, and california's former governor, chief justice earl warren, also held other positions in california government.

6. there is a street near san francisco state university called sloat boulevard, which is named for commodore sloat.

7. if you travel west on sloat boulevard for a long enough time then you will eventually find yourself in the pacific ocean.

8. during the civil war, president lincoln experienced deep personal sorrow at seeing the north and the south locked in such a bitter political struggle.

9. last year my mother ran the boston marathon, but she wasn't able to finish the first mile.

10. this year, she trained carefully and finished the bay to breakers in excellent time.

Exercise 2

In the following sentences, underline words that should be capitalized and draw a line through words that should begin with a lower case letter.

---

1. after speaking with professor callen, i decided to enroll in principles of organizational management and some other courses in business adminstration and finance.

2. i met my new boyfriend at the warfield theatre, which is located on market street near mcdonald's and across the street from walgreen's.

3. a good essay is a piece of writing which must be carefully written, says any good english teacher, but any good, hard-working student can learn how to write well with Time and practice.

4. swallows are birds that fly north, south, East or west to a city in California called capistrano, but those coming from the eastern part of the country have the prettiest trip.

5. members of the feminist movement want to see the equal rights amendment made part of the constitution, while members of the moral majority want to see Abortion made illegal.

6. while I was talking to doctor tarragon about my stomach pains, his nurse came in with some spicy news about his partner, doctor cilantro.

7. when i got the Flu, doctor tarragon told me to take a few tylenol capsules every few hours, but i refused because of the stories i had read in the san franciso chronicle.

8. my Brother-in-law was raised as a catholic, but after attending some of his friends' jewish weddings, he has developed a strong interest in learning about other religions besides his own.

9. i think aunt bessie lived with my grandmother until she was sent to a foster home in nevada which was run by the mormon church.

CAPITALIZATION

Post-Test

Proofread the following paragraph, correcting the capitalization. Insert capitals where they belong and draw a line through capitals that should be small letters.

For christmas my Mother gave me the book, *The complete book of Running*, by James F. Fixx. Mr. Fixx is from the east and is a graduate of Oberlin college. He started running several years ago on a beautiful Spring morning and since then, he has lost 61 pounds. He competed in six Boston marathons, and he won the Connecticut 10,000 meter Championship in his age category. Running is not the only thing James Fixx is good at; he also is a Writer and former Editor of such Magazines as *Life, McCall's,* and *horizon*. He conferred with a number of Doctors in writing his book, as well as the New York academy of sciences and the institute of mental health. Now that I've read and enjoyed the book, I would like to get dad to read it. Theodore G. Klumpp, m.d., claims that people tend to overprotect themselves and that older people should exercise more, and he hopes to establish a Nationwide Exercise Program for the elderly. But I know what my Dad would say! He'd tell me he gets plenty of exercise shoveling snow in Kansas and stays healthy with a shot of russian vodka before he goes to bed each night. Besides, dad thinks most of my ideas are Left-wing and he'd probably think jogging is a plot to overthrow the republican party.

XII. HOMONYMS

Homonyms are words that sound alike but do not mean the same thing and are therefore not spelled alike. These "soundalikes" are not interchangeable. If you use the wrong form in a sentence, you will confuse or mislead your reader—the last thing you want to happen.

YOUR/YOU'RE

Underline all uses of your and you're in the following paragraph.

Your mother called this morning to find out if you're coming for dinner on Sunday. She wants to borrow your souffle dish. You're going, aren't you? She also said that you're welcome to bring your friend, John, but you're going to have to watch your manners because Mrs. Moorhouse will be there, and she is not accustomed to college students and is always nervous around your friends.

1.   Which form shows ownership? _____

2.   Which is the contraction of you + are? _____

On the lines below, write your or you're, as appropriate.

1.   _____ hot tub will be installed Monday.

2.   Do you know where _____ going to put it?

3.   I imagine _____ friends will want to spend the weekends at

       _____ house now.

4.   _____ going to miss _____ quiet weekends alone.

5.   I realize _____ looking forward to relaxing.

6.   _____ chemistry needs work if _____ going to pass the

       class.

7.   _____ the one I want to talk to.

8.   Get _____ feet off the coffee table.

9.   Did you ask _____ sister if she'd go out with me?

10.   If you think _____ smarter than I am, prove it.

90

ITS/IT'S

Underline all uses of *its* and *it's* in the following paragraph.

It's surprising to many people how close the "distant past" really is to us living today. For instance, the American Civil War seems so long ago that it's almost a part of ancient history. Yet its influence lingers with us today in tensions between the North and the South; its battles are still studied by young military officers, and its last veterans died not in the dim past but in the 1950's.

Which form shows ownership? _____

Which form is the contraction of *it + is* or *it + has*? _____

On the lines below, write *its* or *it's* as appropriate.

1. The team won _____ game with _____ chief rivals.

2. Today _____ time to learn that "_____" is a possessive word.

3. The rain certainly took _____ time getting here last winter.

4. Although _____ true that _____ getting rather dark now, I think _____ still too early to go home.

5. _____ sometimes said that France is like a miniature United States; _____ climate and geography are almost as varied as America's.

6. _____ plain to see that the dog obeys _____ master.

7. _____ been four years since I've been to New York.

8. One of SFSU's disadvantages is _____ foggy weather.

9. _____ been a long road for me; _____ taken me ten years to finish college.

THEIR/THERE/THEY'RE

Underline all uses of *their*, *there*, and *they're* in the following paragraph.

Mr. and Mrs. Casey are very staunch Catholics; for that reason, they're upset about their son marrying a Jewish woman. They're concerned that their grandchildren will not have one firm religion to believe in. The Caseys know that there is some basis for their fear, since children of a religiously mixed marriage do have to cope with two religions at one time. However, they've begun to think, "So long as there is love between the parents, how can that harm the children?" In the end, they've reconciled themselves to the marriage.

---

1. Which form shows ownership? _____

2. Which indicates direction or is a way of introducing a thought? _____

3. Which is a contraction of *they + are*? _____

On the lines below, write *their*, *there*, or *they're* as appropriate.

---

1. _____ are three kinds of ghosts in that house.

2. _____ minds weren't on the subject the teacher was talking about.

3. _____ a lot of trouble to people who spend the night.

4. I don't think _____ worth worrying about; _____ bark is worse than _____ bite.

5. _____ is no time like the present to take care of business.

6. They tried to win _____ final game, but _____ was no way they could beat _____ opponents.

WHOSE/WHO'S

Underline all uses of *whose* and *who's* in the following paragraph.

Who's going to the beach with us? We have to decide whose car we're going to take so we can fill it with gas. I already know who's bringing the food and drinks. Susan, whose father runs China Camp, will bring a cooler with cold drinks. Ted, who's Jeff's brother, promised to bring fried chicken and potato salad. But who's agreed to bring the napkins and eating utensils? Whose idea was this anyway?

---

1. Which form shows ownership? _____

2. Which form is the combination of
   $$who + is$$
   or $$who + has?$$ _____

On the lines below, write *whose* or *who's*, as appropriate.

---

1. _____ picking up Sally from the airport?

2. No one knows _____ responsible.

3. He knows _____ fault it is.

4. Can you find out _____ taking Kathy home?

5. The teacher knew all along _____ idea it was to draw the picture on the board.

6. _____ backpack is this?

7. Jeff is one _____ been getting A's on all the tests.

8. We never found out _____ dog spread our garbage all over the neighborhood.

9. Wait until you hear _____ playing at the dance Friday.

TWO/TO/TOO

Underline all uses of *two*, *to*, and *too* in the following paragraph.

      Strikes by employees of mass transit systems incovenience many people. During the last Muni strike, many people had to rearrange their schedules so that they were getting to work earlier than usual and leaving later than usual. Some students found themselves in awkward situations, too, for they were unable to go to school without walking for miles. During the BART strike, too many cars cluttered the freeways and bridges, and this increase in traffic was hazardous to commuters and pedestrians alike. Just these two examples should serve to explain why I am against strikes by Muni and BART employees.

---

1.   Which form indicates the number 2? _____

2.   Which is a prepositon or a part of a verb? _____

3.   Which means either "also" or "very?" _____

On the lines below, write *two*, *to*, or *too* as appropriate.

---

1. It's _____ bad that many people find it _____ easy _____ settle down in front of the television rather than read a book.

2. Over-achievers try _____ hard _____ be perfect at everything they do, but they would be better off trying _____ excel at one or _____ things rather than _____ many at once.

3. My sister's _____ favorite cookie recipes call for _____ much sugar in the ingredients.

4. Pets require lots of care and attention _____ grow into healthy organisms, and plants do, _____.

5. It's _____ bad that plants aren't as stimulating _____ talk _____ as pets, though.

6. My brother is so clumsy that he finds it difficult _____ tie his shoestrings together.

7. " _____ be or not _____ be" is a famous line which _____ many people unthinkingly quote, and there aren't _____ many who can say where it comes from.

8. Children who watch _____ much television usually end up with _____ crossed eyes.

9. _____ succeed in college, a student must be willing _____ work hard and not get discouraged when the workload seems _____ overwhelming.

10. If a student knows how _____ manage time well, then it's not _____ difficult _____ get work done and even have time _____ relax.

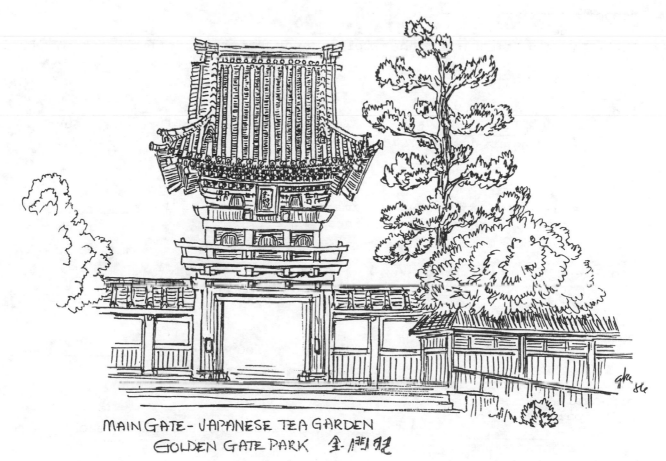

MAIN GATE - JAPANESE TEA GARDEN
GOLDEN GATE PARK 金庸明

The best advice we can give to help you avoid confusing "soundalikes" is to use your dictionary, which will give you not only the correct spelling and definition of a word but also the part of speech the word functions as. All of this information will help you decide which one of the two, or sometimes three, soundalikes fits into your sentence. For example, let's say you are concerned about the words *loose* and *lose*. By looking in the dictionary you will see that *lose* is a verb meaning to mislay or fail to keep while *loose* is an adjective meaning not firmly fastened or not tight.

Using your dictionary, write down the part of speech that the following soundalikes function as. After you have identified and defined them, choose which one best fits the sentence that follows.

accept
except
    Before we _____ the offer, we should first consult a lawyer.

advise
advice
    Her father tried to give her sound _____ but she refused to listen to him.

effect
affect
    Doctors continue to research the _____ alcohol has on the nervous system.

conscious
conscience
    The child returned the stolen candy bar because he had a guilty _____.

lead
led
    We were _____ to our seats just moments before the house lights went down.

loss
lost
    He is still trying to estimate the effects of his _____ on both his personal and business life.

no
know
    I think I _____ the poem well enough to recite it.

patience
patients
    Jennifer realized she would have to focus all her _____ on her math homework.

principle
principal
    The _____ of the high school was also the math teacher who taught me the _____ (s) of geometry.

quit
quite
quiet

Because his grades were dropping, Jack was very _____ in class.

Mary seemed _____ upset after she hung up the phone.

sight
cite
site

The professor asked his students to _____ the references they used in their papers.

The _____ for the new library will be announced next week.

since
sense

We have lived in our apartment _____ December.

lose
loose

Jose thought the team was going to _____ the game.

then
than

Jim is quite a bit taller _____ the rest of his brothers.

weather
whether

_____ or not we go will depend on the _____.

XIII. PLURALS AND POSSESSIVES

SINGULAR AND PLURAL NOUNS

Nouns that refer to one person or thing are singular, while nouns that refer to more than one are plural. This idea is simple enough, but there are several ways of making nouns plural.

SOME RULES FOR FORMING PLURALS

(1)   To make a noun plural, you can often just add an "s" ending:

book	books
horse	horses
movie	movies

(2)   Most nouns ending in o, s, sh, ch, and x add "es" to form plurals:

tomato	tomatoes
class	classes
dish	dishes
church	churches
box	boxes

(3)   Many nouns ending in "y" change the "y" to "i" and add "es" to form their plural:

company	companies
baby	babies

(4)   Still other nouns change form rather than just the ending:

wife	wives
man	men
child	children

(5)   Finally, some nouns don't change form at all:

fish	fish
series	series

Some students confuse plurals and possessives. Apostrophes are not used to show that a noun is plural; they are a punctuation mark that shows possession.

To be absolutely sure you are using the correct plural form, consult a dictionary.

Exercise 1

Use your dictionary to find the plural of the following nouns; then rewrite the sentence replacing the singular noun with the plural noun. You may need to change more than just the noun in writing each sentence.

SOCIETY: A society needs to have effective laws.

THIEF: The thief was caught in the act of purse snatching.

ANALYSIS: An analysis of your dreams might suggest you have hidden fears.

WOMAN: A woman who tripped and fell outside City Hall sued the city.

Note that in the sample four singular sentences, the articles *a, an,* and *the* are all used before singular nouns — *a* society, *the* thief, *an* analysis, *the* woman. The difference between using *a* and *the* can be seen in these two sentences:

A president is an elected official. (Any president, Washington through the incumbent)

The President signed the bill yesterday. (A specific president; the president currently in office)

An is used like *a* in front of most singular nouns beginning with a vowel (*an* analysis). When a noun is plural, never use *a* or *an*; use *the* if you need to use an article.

In addition to *the,* your plural sentences might use other modifiers like *some, several, many,* or a number instead of the singular articles *a* or *an.*

COUNT AND NON-COUNT NOUNS

Most nouns name something you can count, but some name things you cannot count, things you can only measure. For example, if you bought a bag of peanuts, you could count each peanut in the bag, but if you bought a pound of peanut butter, you couldn't count the peanut butter, you could only measure it in ounces. We call words like peanut butter *non-count* nouns, which simply means we do not add "s" to the noun no matter how much of it we are referring to.

One way to determine if a noun is non-count is to put the words *a little bit of* in front of the noun. We also use *much* with non-count nouns. If you don't have *much* homework, it could mean you have one assignment or more. However, we only use *many* with plural count nouns.

Exercise 2

Here is a list of a few of the nouns that are usually non-count. Use each in a sentence.

_____

advice   _____

equipment   _____

evidence   _____

homework   _____

housework   _____

information_____

knowledge   _____

mail   _____

patience   _____

work   _____

POSSESSIVES

The possessive form of a noun shows possession, or ownership. There are several ways to show ownership without changing the noun itself:

the dog of the *boy*   the dog belonging to the *boy*

but a simpler, more common way is to change the noun that does the possessing:

the *boy's* dog

Look at the following phrases and see how the possessive of each italicized noun is formed:

1. the books of the *student* = the *student's* books

   the chairs of the *children* = the *children's* chairs

   the hands of the *clock* = the *clock's* hands

2. the books of the *students* = the *students'* books

   the chairs of the *babies* = the *babies'* chairs

   the testimony of the *witnesses* = the *witnesses'* testimony

   RULE: The possessive of a noun ending in *s* is formed by adding _____ .

With a few exceptions, these two rules include nearly all you will need to know about forming possessives:

* To form the possessive of a noun, add *'s;*
  if the noun already ends in *s*, add *'*.

Note, though, that when a proper noun (a name) ends in *s*, you may choose to add either *'s* or *'* alone, depending on whether you would pronounce the extra *s*. For instance:

Moses' followers   OR   *Moses's* followers

Which is easier to say? In the following phrases, how would you form the possessive of *Charles*?

the bike of *Charles* = _____ bike

the stereo of *Charles* = _____ stereo

* Remember: Do *not* use *'s* when you are only forming a plural.

  CORRECT: Charbroiled *hot dogs* are served here.

  WRONG: Charbroiled *hot dog's* are served here.

Exercise 3

Rewrite each underlined group of words, using apostrophes to show possession.

Example:

He liked *the looks of the fish.*

the fish's looks

He remembered *the names of all of the dogs.*

all of the dogs' names

1. I liked the looks of the car.

2. I liked the looks of the cars.

3. We admired the stars of the movie.

4. We admired the stars of the movies.

5. John was surprised at the skill of the players.

6. He was not surprised at the record of the team.

7. He was not the choice of the people.

8. They liked the selection of goods of the stores.

9. Sheila insulted the pets of her neighbors.

10. Her neighbors accidentally hit the dog of Carlos.

11. It bit the legs of two of the neighbors.

OTHER FORMS OF POSSESSIVES

Here are some guidelines for other types of possessives that you will encounter from time to time.

The following pairs of nouns show joint ownership—that is, two or more people owning the same thing:

the duck belonging to *Sid and Eddie* = *Sid and Eddie's* duck

the piano of *Tina and Al* = *Tina and Al's* piano

RULE: Nouns showing *joint* ownership have _____ added to the noun nearest the thing possessed.

Compare the phrases above with these phrases:

the shoes belonging to *Sid and Eddie* = *Sid's and Eddie's* shoes

the toothbrushes of *Tina and Al* = *Tina's and Al's* toothbrushes

These pairs of nouns show individual ownership. (Sid and Eddie probably do not own the same shoes, nor do Tina and Al use the same toothbrush.)

RULE: Nouns showing *individual* ownership have _____ added to *each* noun.

One more rule: In forming the possessive of a compound noun (a noun composed of more than one word), add *'s* to the last of the words that make up the compound noun:

mother-in-law's suitcase   *commander-in-chief's* uniform

WHEN *NOT* TO USE *'S:*

*   Do *not* use *'s* to form possessive pronouns:

Pronouns	Possessive Pronouns
he	his
she	her/hers
it	its
we	our/ours
you	your/yours
they	their/theirs
my	mine

What possessive pronouns belong in the following example?

This is Doris's book.
This is her book.   This book is _____ .

These are Fred's and Ted's bikes.
These are their bikes.   These bikes are _____ .

Exercise 4

Rewrite each underlined group of words, using apostrophes to show possession.

_____

1. The combined losses of the North and South were the greatest in any American war.

2. The president took away some of the responsibilities of the chief-of-staff.

3. We loved the shoes of George and Sara.

4. She was insulted by the rude remarks of her sister-in-law.

5. I couldn't stand the little mutt of George and Sara.

6. The information of the correspondent-at-large was mostly incorrect.

7. The voyages of Magellan and Columbus were highly successful.

8. The novels of Hemingway and Faulkner are among the most admired in all of modern literature.

9. One of the most famous events in American History is the journey west of Lewis and Clark.

10. Don't forget the present of your mother-in-law.

Exercise 5

Rewrite each underlined group of words using apostrophes to show possession.

1. <u>The images of many professional wrestlers</u> are outrageous.

2. <u>But the image of no one</u> has ever been wackier than that of George Wagner.

3. <u>The nickname of George Wagner</u> was Gorgeous George.

4. He was the most popular wrestler of the Forties and Fifties as well <u>as the biggest television attraction of Los Angeles</u>.

5. He was sometimes called "The Human Orchid," but <u>the color of an orchid</u> seemed drab compared to <u>the magnificent costumes of George</u>.

6. After leaving <u>the house of his father and mother</u> in Houston at age nineteen, George worked at odd jobs and wrestled <u>the other tough kids of Houston</u> at area picnics.

7. He drifted to Oregon, winning <u>the light-heavyweight crown of the state</u>.

8. <u>The income of George</u> was not increasing as a result of these activities, so he decided to become a professional wrestler.

9. In this field <u>the income of the leading wrestlers</u> is determined by their popularity at the box office.

10. <u>The turning point of the career of George</u> came when he hit upon a gimmick that no one else had tried, dressing in outrageously colored clothes with frills and rhinestones.

Exercise 6

Proofread the sentences below. They contain both plural nouns—that is, nouns that do not require apostrophes—and possessive nouns—nouns that do require apostrophes. When a noun is both a plural and a possessive, it requires an apostrophe, of course. Underline any noun ending in *s* and then decide whether it is a possessive. If it is, add the apostrophe in the correct place.

Example:

Charles looked at his clothes and realized that some of his shirts collars were worn.

Charles looked at his *clothes* and realized that some of his *shirts' collars* were worn.

---

1. George soon began wearing the loud outfits that made him famous.

2. His managers daughter created robes for him of fur, feathers, and lace to match his wrestling trunks shocking pink color.

3. His personal valets duties included spraying Georges corner, as well as his opponents face with Chanel No. 9.

4. Gorgeous Georges long, curled, bleached blond hair was his two Hungarian hairdressers handiwork.

5. His hairs true color was brown, and he had always worn it long to imitate George Washingtons long-haired wig.

6. Once, as a result of a lost match, Georges and his wife Cheries heads were shorn of hair, to the astonishment of fourteen thou sand spectators.

7. His imitators efforts to copy him all fell short.

8. The jeers of his critics failed to shake his fans affection.

9. Of course, wrestling fans affections have always been drawn to outlandish costumes and outrageous behavior.

10. Gorgeous Georges fans were no different than those of the numerous other wrestlers who have worn bizarre costumes or taken on strange identities.

POSSESSIVES

Post-Test

Proofread the following passage for possessives, adding apostrophes where necessary to show possession.

Lake Superior is the worlds largest body of fresh water, surpassing all other inland lakes in size except the salt water Caspian Sea. Superior, like the other Great Lakes, was part of the Mississippi Rivers drainage system until Ice Age glaciers gouged deep holes in the rocks. The Glaciers handiwork shows in the shorelines many rugged cliffs (the cliffs heights reach 1500 feet) and in the ancient granite exposed there, among the earths oldest rocks, rivalled only by those at the Grand Canyons base.

Superiors first European visitor, the French explorer Brule, arrived in 1623. Of course, he didn't really discover the lake, as the Chippewa Indians had long lived on the shores of what they called Gitche Gumee. While the Indians name for the lake must have sounded strange to the Europeans, the Indians probably found the Europeans behavior stranger still, as fur traders outposts and the missions of Jesuit priests followed within decades of Brules first visit. The white mans towns and industries made the former Gitche Gumee less and less clean, until by the 1960's the waters oxygen level was so low that fish were suffocating. But in 1972, Canada and the U.S. agreed to clean up the Great Lakes. The two nations cleanup efforts paid off in just a few years, as beaches reopened and fishermens nets again began to fill. The revival of Lake Superior demonstrated once again natures truly amazing ability to repair itself.

XIV. CONTRACTIONS

Besides showing possession, apostrophes also show the omission of one or more letters when words are combined into contractions.

Long Form	Contraction
we will	we'll
they will	they'll
we are	we're
they are	they're
do not	don't
let us	let's
is not	isn't
are not	aren't
should not	shouldn't
will not	won't
The phone is ringing.	The phone's ringing.
My homework is giving me a lot of trouble.	My homework's giving me a lot of trouble.

Exercise 1

Think of five other contractions and write them down, followed by their long forms.

1. _____

2. _____

3. _____

4. _____

5. _____

Exercise 2

In each of the sentences below, form as many contractions as you can. Cross out the words to be contracted and then write the contraction above them.

---

1. When John returns, we will eat dinner.

2. The store is having a sale on sheets and pillowcases, but they will probably be sold out by the end of the week.

3. Even though they are going to be arriving late, they will not be hungry because they will have eaten dinner on the plane.

4. Students should not wait until the night before a test to review all their class notes, for it is not the most effective way of remembering lots of detailed information.

5. The recipes do not call for adding wine, but my mother feels that the final results are not as flavorful without it.

6. We are planning on leaving town for the holidays, but we should not be gone for more than two or three weeks.

7. Most young people are not willing to follow their parents' advice, but they will benefit from at least listening to it.

8. Even though good teachers do not enjoy failing students, they are concerned about being honest with students about the quality of their work.

9. They will not be arriving at the station until 8:00 p.m., so we are going to have dinner at home first and then leave to pick them up.

10. The color of the tablecloth does not match that of the curtains in the dining room, but it will not make any difference because most of our friends do not know anything about good taste, anyway.

Exercise 3

Proofread the sentences below for correct use of apostrophes in contractions.

---

1. Bruno, my friend's dog, didn't turn out to be the vicious beast Id heard about.

2. As a matter of fact, Ive never seen a dog that was more docile and well-behaved.

3. People shouldnt believe all the stories they hear about other people's pets.

4. Most dogs dont take to strangers very well to begin with, but when Bruno didn't even bark at the sight of me, I was most surprised.

5. Bruno isnt allowed in the living room, and its amazing how he doesn't set foot within the boundaries of that particular place.

6. Bruno wont sit still, however, when he sees strangers walking past the front door of my friend's home, and strangers who have weak hearts shouldn't approach unannounced.

7. In addition, Bruno has a curious "roommate," a cat who doesnt move outside of a self-designated area of about twelve inches in diameter.

8. Bruno and the cat didnt get into any territorial hassles when I was there, but I'd bet money that they occasionally must get into playful tiffs of one sort or another.

9. The cat, however, knows that it wouldn't be wise to sink its claws into Bruno's face, for Bruno's mouth is quite large and his teeth aren't much shorter than the cat's claws.

XV. PROOFREADING REVIEWS

PROOFREADING REVIEW 1

Read each of the following sentences carefully. Correct all the errors you find. Some sentences contain more than one error. Some sentences may be completely correct.

1. In our drama class, the students are writing there own plays.

2. Until midterms, your not sure how your classes are going.

3. My brother moved to the south last winter.

4. My husband friends always take there vacations in july.

5. It's cruel to take a kitten away from its mother.

6. Its to bad that Tess parents yelled at her.

7. There going to have difficulty passing the test if their friends dont help them study.

8. She moving to a new house on first street.

9. Your suppose to do your homework before its due.

10. A certain area in golden gate park is block off every sunday just for roller skaters.

11. Last week I saw two accidents in front of the asian art museum. They both happen because some crazy guy skate around the corner to fast.

12. I don't like skating where they're are so many people.

13. The roller skate's cost to much money there.

PROOFREADING REVIEW 2

Read each sentence carefully and correct all the errors that you find. Some sentences contain more than one error, and some contain no errors.

---

1. Until I was in college, I use to drive my sisters car all the time.

2. Even though I believe that criminals should be punished for their crimes, I don't believe in capital punishment.

3. After all, nobodys perfect. When it comes to being punctual.

4. Whenever I go to the library, I get more homework done than I would at home.

5. My english teacher always want us to come to class on time.

6. I guess I understand why she wants us their on time. When I walk in late, I have trouble trying to figure out what the class is discussing.

7. Its difficult to do homework on Sundays when all those great football games are on television.

8. I felt sick yesterday because I had eaten to much chili for dinner. That stuff was hot!

9. The student union contain several places where students' can buy food.

10. Our university pool tables are use by many students. Their usually all busy around lunch time.

11. I have never learn to play pool because I have been to embarrassed to ask anyone to teach me.

12. You're car is making funny noises.   I hope its not going to break down.   You certainly don't have the money to fix it right now.

13. Im suppose to take Francis car to Bobs Auto Shop.

14. Fred is going to move to the east.

CITY LIGHTS ON COLUMBUS

PROOFREADING REVIEW 3

Correct all the errors you find in these paragraphs.

___

A)   Coming to san francisco state university has been a scary experience for Hazel and me.   The huge campus has many different building like two science buildings and the j. paul leonard library.   hazel get lost at least once a week.   Going to her classes.   When shes not in class, she like to watch the odd characters.   She think its fun to talk to them to.   Last week she talk to a guy named Bob, Bobs green hair match his sneakers and many people stopped to talk to him.   Im not as brave as she is.   Because I know Im not suppose to talk to strangers.   They're are sure some strange people at this college.

B)   Sam and Sarah have gathered an unusual collection of pets, one of their favorites are a purple lizard name lisa.   Lisa the lizard use to live in hawaii, but shes adjusting to her new surroundings quite well.   Although she still misses her playmates.   Sams alligator, Alfred, was lonely for a while, to, after he arrived from florida.   Last week, Sam introduce them and there now close friends, its a comfort to them both to have another reptile to talk too.

PROOFREADING REVIEW 4

Correct all the errors you find in these paragraphs.

A)   Learning to write is not easy. I've always had trouble with it. Punctuation, spelling, organization, and much more. If I practiced more, if I wrote more often. I would probably be able to do it with less agony. Getting started is difficult, it is the hardest part. Its something I want to learn, though, because I know I'll get better grades in college if I become a better writer.

B)   My sister love to swim. After a hard day, she enjoy jumping into the water. Splashing her troubles away. She usually goes to the
public pool, the new one, locate on heartwood street. Its heated to about 80 degrees, and the water is crystal clear, to. What amaze her is that their are hardly ever more than three or four people swimming there. Even on a nice sunny day. She can't think of anything she rather do than swim.

PROOFREADING REVIEW 5

Proofread the following passage, correcting any errors you find.

Dear Cindy,

Its been three months since I came out here to the west coast to go too college. I've learned quite a few thing about being a student, I want to share a few of them with you. This advise may help you. When you got to college next year.

First, always know what your expected to do. When you buy the college catalogue, read every word. Because they hold you responsible for it! Last semester, one friend of mine want to take english 50 but since she forgot to take EPT, she couldnt. Now shes behind in her English requirement. I have studied the catalogue so much that I practically have it memorize.

Also, don't be shy. When you get into a class, get to know the person sitting next to you. Sometimes you will be absent, then you'll want to call someone for help. And be sure to get to know you're teachers. There really nice around here, they will help you whenever they can. I go to my math teachers office about once a week and he has really help me alot.

Finally you have to learn to budget your time. Your most valuable possession. My friend nancy really has a problem with this. Since she can't say "no" to her friends. She go out every night and never gets her homeworks done. Then she begs her teacher's to let her have one more day to finish her assignments. She may have to

withdraw from her classes.   I try to do a little homework every
day so it never pile up.

I hope this advice has help you a little bit.   Of course, my
problem are probably different from your's.   But I thought you might
like to know some of the things I've learned at college this year.

Love,

Anita

Just Desserts - Irving